Preface

The species and varieties of Chinese wildlife are tremendous. According to statistics compiled by Chinese zoologists, there are more than 400 species of mammals in China, or nearly 10 percent of the 4,200 species in the whole world. China has 1,183 species of birds, which is more than 13 percent of the world's 8,600 species. This wealth is due not only to China's vast territory (9.6 million square kilometers), but also to its favorable zoo geography. Most countries, big or small, cover a single geographic region. For instance, big countries, such as Canada, the United States of America and the former Soviet Union, belong to the Nearctic Region or the Palaearctic Region only. A few countries, such as India and Mexico, have most of their territory in a single region, but a minor part belongs to a neighboring subregion, hence their faunal species are very rich. However, China is exceptional in that her vast territory is almost equally divided into two regions (the Palaearctic and the Oriental). As a result, her faunal species are incomparably great.

China's unique zoogeographic region extends north to the subarctic zone in the northern part of the Palaearctic Region and south deep into the tropical and subtropical zones in the Oriental Region, thus enabling Chinese fauna to comprise all species of typical arctic animals and typical tropic animals.

The country also extends from the sea west to its interior frontier, crossing gobis, deserts, semideserts, grassy plains, high plains, mountains, hills and mounds, forests, jungles and swamps, each with its peculiar ecological species, unmatched not only by small countries, but even by countries with greater territory. Her rich fauna includes a large number of very rare and precious species, admired by wildlife lovers of many countries. These are what we intend to introduce to readers of this book.

Giant panda in bamboo groves

A half-year-old panda on a tree

Giant Panda, Great Favorite of the World

Whenever the giant panda is mentioned, people naturally think of China, but actually it is not only China's national treasure, but the world's treasure, a great favorite of people all over the world.

This is certainly not exaggeration.

Visitors to the more renowned large zoological gardens of different countries may notice posters hanging on the front of many animal cages, each displaying an eye-catching portrait of a giant panda. Visitors may wonder if it is possible for the zoo to exhibit so many giant pandas, but when they draw closer, they discover that the animals in the cages are not giant pandas at all, but various other precious animals, such as rhinoceroses of Java, Sumatra or India, tigers of Malaysia, south China or Siberia, gorillas of West Africa or orangutans of Indonesia. The posters are not, in fact, common animal labels, but a

new design for wildlife conservation devised by the Worldwide Fund for Nature (WWF), words explaining that zoo animals displaying the giant panda (official emblem of the WWF) are very precious and endangered animals that need the special protection of the peoples of all countries. That is, they belong to the same category of animal as the giant panda — special animals requiring top protection.

This anecdote alone is enough to show the particular position of the giant panda in the minds of the world's leading nature conservationists as well as among international conservation organizations.

Nomenclature

In China the giant panda is generally known as *da xiongmao* or the "great bear-cat," which is its common name. Since the 1930s, when it began to be exhibited in Sichuan Province, different Chinese names have been used, such as *xiongmao* (bear-cat), *maoxiong* (cat-bear), *da xiongmao* (great bear-cat), *da maoxiong* (great cat-bear), all mixed together and continuing in use to the present.

Its name in ancient Chinese books was mo, or tapir, a name now specifically applied to an animal that lives in Central and South America, and therefore no longer applicable to the giant panda.

In its homeland people call it *bai xiong* (white bear) or *hua*

Having his meal

xiong (multicolored bear). Its German and Russian names are also linked with "bear". When zoologists, in 1869, were trying to decide what to name this animal, it was first erroneously put into *Ursus*, the genus of bear, and given the scientific name of *Ursus melanolecus*, or black-and-white bear.

When taxonomists later discovered this was a mistake, they corrected it to *Ailuropoda melanoleuca*, or black-and-white short-tailed panda, the name in current use.

As for its Chinese name, the earliest name, *xiongmao* (bear-cat), was also the result of a misunderstanding, because the original name *maoxiong* (cat-bear), was wrongly read from right to left instead of from left to right.

Even though some taxonomists insisted on changing it back to *maoxiong* (cat-bear) or da *maoxiong* (great cat-bear), because it resembled a bear more than a cat, people still habitually called it da xiongmao, with newspapers and popular journals following suit, until finally the name beyond changing. Current practice is to use *da maoxiong* as the academic (scientific) name and *da xiongmao* as the popular name.

Classification and Morphology

Disputes between Chinese and foreign scholars over classification have been going on for years. Many foreign scholars think the giant panda should be included in Ursidae, the bear family, or should be regarded as a species of bear, while some Chinese scholars insist it belongs to a family of its own, the Ailuropodidae, an idea not yet universally accepted.

Generally a giant panda is slightly smaller than a black bear, with a body length of 150 to 170 centimeters and a weight of 100 to 125 kilograms, reaching more

Plucking bamboo leaves

A female giant panda caressing her young

than 180 kilograms for the largest. The difference between male and female size is not great. Both sexes have very short tails (12 to 15 centimeters) and short, poorly developed whiskers. These characteristics resemble the bear's. Yet there are many differences between giant pandas and bears, especially as to tooth structure.

The panda's incisors are weak and irregular, unsuitable for cutting; the crown of its molars is wider and flatter and its premolars are much larger than the bear's.

Its carnassial teeth are not shaped like a carnivore's at all. This peculiar tooth structure resulted in modification of the shape of the skull, which became short and wide with a snout shorter than a bear's, but the cheekbone is much wider than a bear's, similar to that of a lion or tiger. All these changes resulted from many years of eating hard bamboo instead of meat.

Other peculiarities include a small protuberance on the inner rim of its front paw, like a sixth finger, and the shape and length of its claws are not bearlike, but racoonlike.

Chinese zoologists are convinced that there are enough peculiarities to create a separate family (Ailuropodidae) for the giant panda, but foreign scholars think otherwise. They say there are barely enough peculiarities to set up a subfamily (Ailuropodinae) under the bear family (Ursidae).

So goes the disagreement over the classification of the giant panda.

Since giant pandas are so popular in zoological gardens as well as publications all over the world, there's no need to describe its general appearance, but some additional description may be helpful.

Giant panda pictures usually show a black head contrasting with a white body. Actually the head is not pure black, but brownish black, and the body is not pure white, but milky white. A peculiar brown-and-white specimen was found in the Qin Mountains in Shaanxi Province in 1985, the first nonblack-and-white giant panda on record.

A cute face

Resting on a trunk

Distribution, Population and Numerical Variation

The distribution range of giant pandas includes the Chinese provinces of Sichuan, Gansu and Shaanxi.

In Sichuan the range is chiefly in the western and northern parts of the province, with the Qionglai Mountains as the center of distribution, expanding southward to Tianquan and Lushan counties and the Daliang Mountain Range, and northward to Heishui and Songpan counties and the Min Mountain Range.

From north to south the range extends nearly 600 kilometers; from east to west it's 200 to 300 kilometers.

In Gansu the range is limited to the counties of Wudu and Wenxian in the province's south. From there the range extends eastward, reaching the counties of Foping and Yangxian on the southern slopes of the Qin Mountains in Shaanxi Province. It is not known exactly how many giant pandas are living in this vast area, as no full-scale survey has been made. The general estimate is fewer than a thousand.

To protect these animals, over a dozen nature reserves have been set up in the last ten to twenty years.

In broad terms the giant panda's ecology is specialized as to habitat and feeding habit. The two are closely connected.

Briefly, its habitat is the great bamboo forests in the high mountains of western China, and its feeding habit refers to its pattern of feeding chiefly on bamboo (leaves, stems and shoots). How did an animal originally belonging to the Carnivora become a bamboo eater, and why is its distribution and ecological range limited to this district? The answer may be that in the long struggle for existence the giant panda became a loser and a hermit. It lacked powerful defensive weapons, sensory organs and fighting spirit. For these reasons

. Climbing up higher for a good view

it was not only far less powerful than the tigers, leopards and wolves, but also became inferior to bears.

In fact, it was not even a fair competitor to large ungulates. Moreover, the continued expansion of human societies dealt it harder blows. Giant pandas originally living in south and east China probably became extinct long, long ago. Remnants in other areas were then forced to retreat until they reached the high-mountain bamboo forests in western China, where human settlements and other strong opponents were comparatively few. This haven of peace provided not only security, but an inexhaustible storehouse of food. The panda could live there right up to today.

Limited by its peculiar feeding habit, the giant panda is unable to leave the bamboo forest belt. If pressed by hunger, it might come down from the high cliff to seek food in villages lower down, but it almost never raids farm crops or attacks any livestock. It is

Two half-year-old pandas amusing each other

months) is shorter than for bears, but longer than for lesser pandas; delivery is earlier than for bears, but later than for lesser pandas.

Each litter consists of one or two babies only. The newborn is conspicuously small. While the mother weighs more than a hundred kilograms, the baby weighs only about a hundred grams. The ratio (1:1,200) is unlike that of any other species of wild animal except the marsupials. The ratio for bears is 1:600-800. The higher the ratio, the less consumption for the mother and the better chance to seek food and escape from enemies.

Maturity for the giant panda is six to seven years, and its longest life span may reach 30 years; specimen kept by the Beijing Zoo holds just such a record.

therefore a wild beast totally harmless to people.

Habitually, it is mostly nocturnal. It usually climbs a tree to rest on thick branches or in holes in the daytime. When night comes, it spends most of its time seeking food on the ground, eating while walking and emptying its bowels simultaneously once in a while.

Gestation (four to five

Apes and Monkeys

A stump-tailed macaque

Apes and monkeys are the animals of most interest to both adults and children, because of their close relationship to man. All belong to the same order, the primates. Within the primates the higher class anthropoids resemble human beings in many respects, morphologically, physiologically, psychologically, ethologically, etc. Are we not drawn to them because we discern images of ourselves in them?

They have become most popular animals in zoos and circuses and also objects of study indispensable for research organizations, institutions of higher education, and medical units.

In introducing the rare and precious animals of China, apes and monkeys are naturally the main ones.

Before we make individual introductions, it is necessary to give a general account.

According to the basic principles of zoogeography, the equator is the center of distribution for primates and their range is limited to tropical areas to the north and south. Thus species and populations of apes and monkeys decrease the farther one gets from the distribution center.

Since the greater part of Chinese territory is located in the northern temperate zone, Chinese primates cannot compare with those of countries located in tropical zones so far as species and populations are concerned.

Next, the higher the species (such as the large anthropoids) or the lower the species (such as the lemurs and lorises), the more specialized they become. These specialized animals have higher habitat requirements and lower migratory ability and adaptability. In contrast the middle-class monkeys (such as langurs and macaques) adapt more easily to the vast temperate zones, where temperatures are lower and the ecology is more complicated, because they possess more complex feeding habits and stronger resistance to cold weather and are likely to be both terrestrial and arboreal.

For these reasons the great majority of Chinese primates belong to the middle class, with only few in the lower classes of pseudo or half monkeys or the higher classes of anthropoids.

China has 18 to 20 species of primates, including two species of lorises (loris and pigmy loris), six species of macaques (common macaque, pig-tailed macaque, Taiwan macaque, Assamese macaque, red-faced stump-tailed macaque, and hairy-faced stump-tailed macaque), four or five species of langurs (white-headed langur, black langur, long-tailed langur, Phayre's langur, bonneted langur?), three species of golden monkeys (typical golden monkey, black golden monkey, gray golden monkey), three or four species of gibbons (white-handed gibbon, white-browed gibbon, black-crested gibbon and white-cheeked black gibbon?).

Six of these species are endemic to China and also rare and precious species, therefore worthy of introduction individually. Two other species, owing to uncertainty as to their native haunt and classification, are listed with a question mark.

Golden Monkeys

Through presentations, purchase, exchange or lending, some well-known endemic rare and precious Chinese animals have been exhibited to the public in foreign countries in recent years. The animals most welcomed and valued by foreigners are giant pandas and golden monkeys.

We have already discussed the giant panda. As for the golden monkey, although it is not so famous as the giant panda, it is almost as celebrated abroad.

Despite the many kinds of apes and monkeys in different countries, including some very outstanding species -- some very big in stature, others very beautiful or fantastic in looks or very clever and skilful in performance, thereby gaining fame in foreign zoos — the Chinese golden monkey, since its exhibition abroad in recent years, has quickly beaten many of its rivals and risen to the top of the competition.

The golden monkeys of China have won the championship not only because they possess so many fine qualities such as a smart and attractive appearance, comparatively large stature, liveliness and agility but, more significantly, because they are rare and difficult to obtain.

As a matter of fact, the popularity of the Chinese golden monkey had spread out of China long, long ago. At the time giant pandas became known abroad, people in other countries had already heard that China owned a very valuable monkey known as the golden monkey. Its discovery by scientists almost coincided with that of the giant panda. The native haunts of both animals are the sparsely settled thick alpine forest regions in far west China, so whenever foreigners talked about the giant panda, they associated it with the golden monkey,

elevating both to equal popularity. Giant pandas were exported out of China much earlier, however. Both animals are found only in China, and both are under strict control, with sale forbidden. Golden monkeys had never been presented as gifts to foreign friends, so it was even more difficult to catch sight of a golden monkey outside China.

Whereas the first giant panda reached America in 1936, no foreign zoo exhibited golden monkeys until the end of the 1980s. Even now only a few European and American zoological gardens, through short-term loans, have been able to give their visitors a look at this monkey, and the loans have been limited to the typical species of golden monkeys *(Rhinopithecus roxellanae)*, not the two other species, which are not easy to see even in China.

Strictly speaking, the golden monkey should be limited to a single species, but the genus of snub-nosed monkeys, *Rhinopithecus,* to which golden monkeys belong, consists of four species. Though all are referred to as golden monkeys, in reality golden monkey should refer only to *Rhinopithecus roxellanae.* The others have different species names.

The name *roxellanae* comes

Yunnan (or black) golden monkey

was admired. Actually, the "beauty" is limited to the long shiny golden hair draped over its shoulders. Its face cannot compare to the queen's. It has a small nose with upturned nostrils on a blue face. Thus it is definitely absurd to borrow Queen Roxellanae's name! It should be named golden-haired monkey, since long golden hair covers the neck, chest and shoulders of the monkey, especially the males. The shoulder hair may be as long as 40 to 50 centimeters. Silvery, whitish, grayish, brownish and other color hair grows on other parts of the body. The hair, the big black eyes and two big lumps at the corners of its mouth are quite attractive.

It is a stalwart class of monkeys. A male may be 80 centimeters tall and weigh 30 to 35 kilograms, its tail as long as 60 to 70 centimeters; the females are generally one third smaller than the males.

This description fits the typical species of golden monkey. Nontypical species are obviously

from the name of a very beautiful and charming ancient queen, indicating how much the "beauty" of the golden monkey

16

different, some chiefly black, others chiefly gray, hence called black golden monkey and gray golden monkey. The names are improper since there is no golden hair on the body at all. It would be better to rename them black snub-nosed monkey and gray snub-nosed monkey. There is an ongoing debate about the classification of the monkeys' species. Several years ago some scholars declared that even though gray monkeys and black monkeys differed in color from the typical golden species, their basic morphological structures differed very little; therefore they regarded the different-colored monkeys as subspecies of the typical species, deciding that China has only one species and three subspecies of golden monkeys. However, after more studies later on, we discovered other different elements, such as: (1) The ratio of tail length to body length differs, in some very much; (2) newborn babies differ in color right from the beginning; (3) ecological conditions and living habits differ greatly. For these reasons more people now believe they are really three independent species.

As for the native haunts and ecological habitats of the different golden monkeys, the native haunt of the first (typical) species often overlaps that of the giant panda. Both are largely located in the mountainous regions of several provinces in west China, principally the Qionglai Mountain Range and Min Mountain Range in western and northern Sichuan Province; hence this species is sometimes also named Sichuan golden monkey. However, it is also found in the Qin and Motian mountain ranges in southern Shaanxi Province and southern Gansu Province and Mount Dashennongjia in western Hubei Province. The second species is found only on the Fanjing Mountain in northeastern Guizhou Province; therefore it is also known as the Guizhou golden monkey. The third species is found only in the Great Snow Mountains in northern Yunnan Province; hence it is also called the Yunnan golden monkey. Since their native haunts are different, their ecological habitats also differ in many respects. In western Sichuan Province golden monkeys often move around in the alpine coniferous forests at 2,800 to 3,200 meters above sea level and sometimes move down to mixed coniferous and deciduous broadleaf forest belts. Although the area is located in the southern part of the north temperate zone, it is very cold in winter, because the mountains are very high and snow-capped. The monkeys grow long, thick hair to resist the cold, and their activities are not hindered.

The monkeys are highly gregarious. A group may consist of at least 30 to 50 animals, often up to 200 to 300, or even more. The area of activity for each group varies from 10 to 20 square

Phayre's langur

kilometers depending upon the size of the group. Daily distances may reach 1,000 or 2,000 meters, and if they encounter enemies, especially hunters, they flee dozens of kilometers away. Their natural enemies include leopards, clouded leopards, golden cats, black bears and yellow-throated martens. Since they can move about in the trees with great agility and rapidity, they are very difficult to catch.

Their feeding habits are basically similar to those of the langurs, eating chiefly the buds, leaves and seeds of various plants and also wild fruits and tender bark, occasionally taking some living creatures, such as insects, young birds, and bird eggs.

Golden monkeys are arboreous, seldom leaving the trees' high crowns, but when green grass appears, they come down to enjoy the tender food. Their mating season occurs chiefly in autumn. The gestation period lasts more than six months, with baby monkeys born mainly between March and May.

In Guizhou, the gray golden monkey is limited to Fanjing Mountain in the counties of Jiangkou, Yinjiang and Songtao. The mountain covers approximately 40,000 hectares and rises to 2,510 meters above sea level. The range of the Guizhou golden monkey is chiefly between 1,400 and 1,800 meters, so it may be regarded as a midalpine animal. The lowest level of their range is evergreen broadleaf forest at about 800 meters above sea level; the highest level may reach mixed deciduous-evergreen forest at over 2,000 meters above sea level. The largest group ever seen consists of about 100 monkeys; the smallest group, fewer than ten. Their daily activity range varies between 4 and 13 square kilometers, depending upon the size of the group.

The Yunnan golden monkey is

limited to the northwestern part of the province, sandwiched between the Jinsha (upper Yangtze) and Lancang (Mekong) rivers in the high mountains from Weixi to Deqen counties. A few are also said to live at Markam in Tibet and Batang in Sichuan Province. The golden monkeys living in this particular region have obvious differences in ecological habitats and living habits from the two other species of golden monkeys. Since their habitats are higher, with different temperature and vegetation, the monkeys vary as to their cold resistance ability and feeding habit.

The Yunnan monkeys, living in dark coniferous forests at 3,300 to 4,000 meters above sea level, have developed comparatively simple feeding habits, limited chiefly to the green portion of plants. They are the only monkey species that feeds on the greenish portion of coniferous trees. The reason they inhabit so high a place is chiefly because they feed mainly on pine creepers and pine and fir needles that grow on tree crowns at this altitude.

The temperature is far lower than in Sichuan and Guizhou provinces, averaging only 4.7 degrees centigrade. The number of days below zero reach 140 to 200 in a year. Frostless days number only 80 to 90. There is a distinct breeding season. The majority of baby monkeys are born in July and August. The Yunnan golden monkey groups are far smaller than the Sichuan groups. The largest groups ever seen number only a few dozen each.

Since the Yunnan golden monkeys have the smallest population of the three species, they are one of the rarest monkey species in the world. According to a survey, there were over 800 in the Baima Snow Mountains in the early 1960s. During the ten-year chaos of the "cultural revolution," which spoiled the peace and order of the mountain region, a large number of monkeys were hunted and killed; up to the mid-1980s there were still merchants who engaged in the illegal purchase of monkey pelts and bones. Even though the Yunnan golden monkey has been designated as a first-grade national protected animal and its native haunts have been made nature reserves, its numbers are estimated at only 200 to 400. Its prospects look like very precarious unless protective measures are stringently enforced.

A Langur and Two Macaques

The white-headed langur, the hairy-faced stump-tailed macaque and the eastern Hebei macaque are well-known primates endemic to China.

The white-headed langur (*Presbytis leucocephalus*) was discovered and scientifically named as late as 1957, becoming one of the latest species of high-class mammals to be

A female white-headed langur nursing her young

White-headed langur with her young (yellow colored)

discovered. Since it is a very rare and endangered species, it is rarely seen in zoological gardens. Seven white-headed langurs are kept in five Chinese zoos; none has ever been kept in a foreign zoo.

White-headed langurs inhabit a very narrow and small area, being limited to parts of the four counties of Fusui, Chongzuo, Longzhou and Ningming in southwestern Guangxi Zhuang Autonomous Region. The total area is less than 500 square kilometers, and the total population numbers only about 600, according to a survey made in 1967-1977.

The ecological habitat of the white-headed langur is basically karst hills where there are limestone cliffs and thick jungles.

In the daytime the monkeys exercise and seek food in the jungles; at night they retire and sleep in crevices and caves of the stony cliffs.

Physically, the white-headed langur is similar to all other langurs — with comparatively small head, slender limbs and body, and a tail longer than the body. A tuft of white hair crowns the head, and females have a patch of white hair on the hip.

Newborn baby langurs are golden yellow, gradually changing with age to the adult coloring of black body and limbs, white head, and white hair draping over the neck and shoulders. The tuft of hair on top of the head is also white; the upper half of its tail is black, the lower half white. Some white hair also grows on the back of its hands and feet. All these are apparently camouflage colors for jungle-dwelling animals.

The largest of seven specimens collected from

Macaques looking at the Suoxiyu Waterfall in Hunan Province

Guangxi Zhuang Autonomous Region is 61.4 centimeters long. The longest tail is 89 centimeters, and the heaviest weight is 9.45 kilograms. These figures correspond roughly with those of other varieties of langurs, but body colors and patterns differ considerably. The white-headed langur is one of the more good-looking.

The hairy-faced stump-tailed macaque is very different from the white-headed langur. Fundamentally, macaques and langurs are two entirely different types of monkeys, macaques being more robust, vigorous, mischievous and ferocious, and the langurs more slender, agile, light and mild. Their feeding habits are also different. Langurs have no cheek pouch. They eat more for each meal. They have bigger stomachs, but thinner stomach walls, hence a weaker digestive power. They can eat fresh leaves, light twigs, wild fruits, etc. and easily fall ill if they eat other things.

Macaques, however, are omnivorous animals, able to eat all kinds of coarse foods. They store food in cheek pouches for slow chewing and digestion.

Macaques have many species. The hairy-faced stump-tailed macaque, a species found only in China, is well-known in other countries. Since its scientific name is *Macaca thibetana,* it is also called Tibetan macaque. It was given its scientific name in the last century, when it was mistakenly believed to have originated in Tibet. Actually it is found in Xikang and western Sichuan, hence zoological gardens call this monkey Sichuan monkey. Formerly it was believed to inhabit only high mountains in western China, but later

investigation discovered a much wider range of distribution, including provinces and regions in central and south China, such as Guangxi, Jiangxi, Anhui, Hubei and Hunan. The populations in two places are the most famous. One is Mount Emei in Sichuan, where monkeys harassing visitors became a problem hard to deal with. Even so, the monkeys continue to receive fairly good protection. Their population was estimated as at least 350 in 1985.

The other place is Mount Huang, also a famous tourist attraction in Anhui Province. The monkey populations at scenic resorts are spoiled animals, well-known in China for causing a number of mishaps in recent years.

Red-faced macaques resting on tree branches

The hairy-faced stump-tailed macaque, as indicated by its name, has two morphological characteristics. One is a hairy face, the other a short tail; adult monkeys, both male and female, have long hair on both cheeks and chin, like a big beard. Big males, in particular, have luxuriant beards, hence they are nicknamed "hairy uncle" in southern Hunan Province.

Common macaques' tails are nearly equal to one third their body length, whereas the hairy-faced and a red-faced macaque's tail is only one eighth to one tenth its body length. The hairy-faced macaque has a bigger body than the common macaque. The males are 70 to 80 centimeters long, with a tail 7 to 10 centimeters long, and weigh 15 to 20 kilograms. A few may weigh over 30 kilograms. It is a bright and clever monkey, easily domesticated.

The eastern Hebei macaque has the most northerly range and is a rare subspecies of the common macaque.

The common macaque, better known as Bengal macaque or rhesus monkey, is widely distributed with many subspecies common in many provinces in central and south China. They are not rare and precious, except for the eastern Hebei subspecies, which has a range particularly far to the north. While most macaque subspecies are distributed in tropical and subtropical areas, this subspecies alone is found in the northern part of the north temperate zone, approaching the subarctic zone. The northern part of Hebei Province is at north latitude 40° 50', therefore this monkey's range is the most northerly in the world. Since the location is so far north, the monkey may possibly have the greatest endurance against cold. Temperatures often drop to more than 20 degrees centigrade below zero in winter. How the monkey populations living in the mountain forests withstand the long winters is an intensely interesting question.

Another question is how these monkeys, originally inhabiting warm areas in the south, could have leaped over seveal provinces to appear in a northern territory fundamentally without primate species. Years ago it was said they were introduced there to "guard" the royal tombs. For a long time such an argument sounded reasonable, for there were other animals (such as sika

Pig-tailed macaques at Yunnan forest

deer, roe deer and black bears) living in the mountain forests of the East Tomb district that had likely been introduced from other places. However, in the last few years, since more macaque populations have been found in some districts of northern Henan and southern Shanxi provinces, another theory has alleged that the macaques in eastern Hebei Province moved gradually from the southern provinces in a long historical process. In my opinion, this is the more likely possibility.

Quite a number of Chinese and foreign scholars are worried about the fate of this rare and precious monkey subspecies with high academic value and a stirring history. They wonder whether it is on the brink of extinction, for its original population was very small, and proper protective measures have been lacking in recent years. As a result, the numbers are negligible.

At the end of the 1980s a few members of academic circles visited eastern Hebei Province to look for any trace of the subspecies, and returned disappointed. Practically no one caught sight of the monkey. At most they got vague news from a few persons knowledgeable about the situation.

In the spring of 1988 a very few were said to remain on Mounts Mao and Liuliping in the counties of Pinggu and Xinglong, so the subspecies may not yet be extinct.

Gibbons

Three or four of the nine or ten species of gibbons, all in South and Southeast Asia, are found in China. Their native habitats are in

the provinces of Hainan and Yunnan. Population numbers are small.

As for their morphological characteristics, gibbons first of all are tailless. In the course of evolution the animal got rid of its tail, a major symbol of monkeys. Next, the forelimbs (arms) are particularly long, far exceeding the hind limbs; therefore when it stands on the ground, it can easily touch the ground with its hand (which is longer than the foot). It has a very small, light and lively body.

In addition it has a sound sac on its throat that helps it to call loudly. Body colors of gibbons are comparatively complicated, including black, brown, yellow, milky white, and silvery gray. Colors differ not only between species, but also between males and females, old and young of the same species.

One Chinese gibbon is the white-handed gibbon (*Hylobates lar*), which was known only in Southeast Asian countries, but

White-handed gibbon

later found in China as well. Three colonies were discovered in Lancang County of Yunnan Province in the mid-1970s, then more were found in Menglian and Cangyuan counties near the Sino-Myanmar border. All were few in number and have scarcely been seen since the 1980s.

The white-handed gibbons, similar to other species of gibbons, live in small families consisting of a pair of adults with three or four young and inhabit thick forests. The territory of each family may be as small as 13 hectares or more than 133 hectares.

They move about in the upper branches of tall trees, feeding on wild fruits, leaves, buds, insects and bird eggs, and only occasionally come down to drink or seek food. They have no fixed mating season. Newborns may be found in any month of the year. They reach maturity when six or seven years old. Young males and females are driven out of the family when approaching adulthood, to seek suitable mates and form new families.

Their life span is about 25 years in the wild and may reach 33 in zoological gardens. Their principal enemies in the wild are pythons in the forests and big birds of prey in the sky.

The white-handed gibbon is the smallest of the gibbons and has an average weight of only 5.5 kilograms, at most not over 6.5 kilograms. When it is standing on the ground, its height may reach 62 centimeters. The length of its arms stretched horizontally may reach 76 centimeters.

Its body colors include both light (grayish yellow and light yellow) and dark (black and brown). Its black face is encircled with a ring of white hair that looks rather comical. The backs of its hands and feet are white, hence the name white-handed gibbon. In Chinese it is called the white-palmed gibbon, but this is incorrect, for it is white-handed, not white-palmed. Some people have thus renamed it in Chinese.

The white-browed gibbon has two stripes of white hair on the forehead, making it look white-browed.

Other species have white hair in circles, half circles and horizontal bars on their faces, making it very easy to confuse them with the white-browed gibbon. In addition, some male gibbons have black hands and feet, while the females have white hands and feet, making it hard to distinguish them.

The white-browed gibbon has another characteristic: a flat crown without tufted hair, but with some hair growing backwards. It is comparatively large, with a body length of 52 to 53 centimeters and weight of 7 to 8 kilograms.

Rare in China, it is found only in the counties of Yingjiang, Lianghe, Tengchong in western Yunnan Province near the Sino-Myanmar border. According to investigations conducted in the last few years, only some 50 gibbons remained in the forests

A white-browed gibbon calling her mate

in the vicinity of Yingjiang; therefore it may be regarded as the least numerous species among Chinese apes and monkeys.

This ape regularly stays in thick forests, hiding in the lower thickets of thorns and remaining calm even when someone approaches. Only if attacked, will they take to their heels with great rapidity through the upper layer of trees.

Observers are astonished at how they can leap many rods and land on another tree.

People have discovered certain regularities in their morning shouts. On clear and sunny mornings they always shout, but on cloudy or rainy days they seldom shout. Before shouting, an adult animal climbs up a tall withered tree, looks around in all directions for some minutes, then begins shouting. His partners follow, then others join in the chorus one after another. The chorus may last some quarters of an hour. After all is over, the apes seek food following a certain route. Besides eating the buds and leaves of plants, they catch and eat insects, small birds and bird eggs. They are totally helpless in swimming. Once a gibbon fell into a pond and lost control. He would have drowned if not rescued in time.

The black gibbon is also called black-crested gibbon because it has an eye-catching blackish crown of hair on its head. However, this ape is not always black. When young, both male and female are light yellowish, turning blackish gradually after six months of age. The male retains its black color throughout its life, but the female's color gradually lightens after adulthood (six to seven years old), until it turns milky yellow or grayish yellow, except for a patch of black on its crown and neck.

The black gibbon has a wider distribution and larger population than other Chinese gibbons.

Its range includes Hainan Island and south-central parts of Yunnan Province. Unfortunately, both populations are in sad condition, especially the gibbon population on Hainan Island.

In the early 1950s they were found in all 12 counties on the island, numbering more than 2,000. After many mishaps, including heavy deforestation and uncontrolled poaching, they could be found in only two places, the Bawang and Limu mountains. Only a few dozen are said to remain.

The white-cheeked black gibbon (*H.leucogenys*), previously regarded as a subspecies of the black gibbon, is now recognized as an independent species. It's native haunts are at Mengla and Shangyong in Yunnan's Xishuangbanna. Its population of over 1,000 in the 1960s is down to 100, owing to too much deforestation (the original 1.1 million hectares has been reduced to 0.53 million hectares). These figures indicate that the gibbon species in China are the most endangered of all Chinese apes and monkeys. They face the danger of total extinction unless special protective measures are taken in time.

Albino form of stump-tailed macaque

A small herd of David's deer

David's Deer — Valuable Chinese Cervidae

It is well-known throughout the world that China has the greatest number of deer genera and species, especially rare and precious species, in the world.

Ranking first among her rare and precious species is David's deer. As early as the Zhou Dynasty (11th century B.C.), when King Wu launched an expedition against the tyrant Zhou, David's deer, as the mount of Jiang Ziya, commander of the expeditionary forces, had become famous throughout the country.

The Discovery of David's Deer

The deer's original name in ancient Chinese literature was *milu*, and its popular name was *sibuxiang*. In English it is known as David's deer because it was discovered by a French priest, Father Armand David, in a royal hunting park near Peking in the late 19th century.

Father David was sent to China in 1861 to promote religion.

However, as an amateur zoologist, his interest in studying zoology was much greater than his interest in religious propagation. In the years he lived in China he discovered and introduced to the outside world the giant panda, golden monkey and *sibuxiang*.

Of these, the discovery of *sibuxiang* is particularly interesting.

When David was in Peking, he heard large numbers of rare and precious birds and beasts were kept in an imperial hunting park called Nanhaizi in the southern suburb of the city. The best-known animal was a strange one called *sibuxiang*, which greatly aroused his interest. However, he dared not visit the place, because entrance was strictly forbidden. Finally, one day in the autumn of 1865, he made up his mind to try his luck.

A notice outside the park warned that intruders would be arrested and beheaded. He paced the length of the wall until he found a mound, which he climbed to take a look inside the park. He quickly discovered a herd of deer grazing on the shores of a lake. With his zoological talent he immediately recognized these deer were very different from all known species, especially their antlers and tails. He was reminded of a descriptive saying he had heard about this animal: "Tail like a donkey's, but not a donkey; hooves like a cow's, but not a cow; neck like a camel's, but not a camel; antlers like a deer's, but not a deer." This description had given the animal the name *sibuxiang*, "four unliked." Of special note was "antlers like a deer's, but not a deer." Although the antlers looked very like a deer's, there was one obvious difference, in that antlers commonly have a brow tine extending from the forehead, but those of the *sibuxiang* did not.

In truth the *sibuxiang*'s antlers do have a brow tine, but unlike ordinary antlers with a single brow tine extending straight out,

the *sibuxiang*'s brow tine has branches like the main stem, so people without professional knowledge didn't believe these were deer antlers.

As for the tail, though not so long as a donkey's tail, it looks more like a donkey's tail than like the usually very short deer's tail.

Nearly half a meter long, it can reach the deer's heels, and it can swing to and fro. The *sibuxiang*, domesticated for ages, may have learned to swing its tail to sweep away insects, which may have contributed to the growth of the tail. Whether the tail of wild *sibuxiang* in prehistoric times was

as long and the hair at the tail's end as full and luxuriant as nowadays we may never know.

The hooves are big and wide, the two petals widely separated and a suspended hoof well developed. This is an animal suited to live on swampy wetlands or the banks of rivers

Two male David's deer lying on mud in Nanhaizi Park

and lakes.

David's deer is slightly smaller than a wapiti, but just as robust. The male is 1.15 to 1.22 meters tall at the shoulder and weighs 180 to 200 kilograms. The female is a quarter to a fifth smaller. The young animal is light redish with yellowish-white spots, which disappear when the winter coat is grown. The adult is reddish brown with an obvious black back stripe, but the winter coat turns to brownish gray with a layer of long, thick hair and a layer of soft, fine hair. The deer has a long face, giving it a sad and melancholy look.

When David stood on the mound looking at the herd of *sibuxiang*, he felt these were deer rarely seen and worth study, but he did not know that this herd was almost the only remnant herd in the world, for wild populations of this species of deer had become extinct long before. It's hard to determine exactly when it became extinct. Some people believe it was

extinct as early as the Han Dynasty (206 B.C. to A.D. 220). Fossil evidence indicates it multiplied enormously only in the Shang and Zhou dynasties, when its distribution range reached the Qiantang River in the south and the peat marshland in the eastern suburb of present Beijing in the north, with the central and lower reaches of the Yellow River as the center. By the end of the Zhou Dynasty (11th century-221 B.C.), the *sibuxiang* began to diminish, its population continuing to dwindle until it vanished in the Han Dynasty. However, some scholars believe the deer could still be found after that time, as there were remnant herds in seacoast regions of Haimen, Nantong and Taixian even in the early Qing Dynasty (1644-1911).

It was believed that the *sibuxiang* populations in central China (middle and lower reaches of the Yellow River), site of the earliest human civilization, might have been extinguished by the

early settlers more than 1,000 years ago, but the populations living along the Huai and Yangtze rivers were compelled only to move eastward; thus small numbers might have remained in the desolate seacoast regions as late as the last days of the Ming Dynasty (1368-1644) and early days of the Qing Dynasty. The herd in Nanhaizi Hunting Park might have come from this region. Thanks to the 200 to 300 deer kept by the hunting park, the species was preserved.

When Father David sought a few specimens, it was not because he understood how rare and hard to get this deer was, but chiefly because he believed it was a new species. For this reason, he devised all sorts of schemes, until he finally attained his goal by applying a worldly knack, that is, bribery. In a few months' time, on a bitter cold, windy night in January 1866, this Catholic father, wearing his heavy vestment, arrived at the outer wall of the hunting park by appointment.

A female David's deer with her calf

A park guard and he conducted a deal over the wall. Father David first handed over ten ounces of silver; the guard then handed over a deer head and pelt. Again Father David handed over ten ounces of silver, and again the guard handed over a deer head and pelt. Satisfied, both withdrew.

After examination by the Paris Natural History Museum the specimen was confirmed as a new genus and species of deer. Therefore it was given the name David's deer or *Elaphurus davidianus*. Since the new animal had very strange characteristics and was so dramatically discovered and acquired, the news spread quickly and widely, causing many European countries to make requests for it from the Qing government, which responded by sending dozens of David's deer to western Europe in the following years to be exhibited in British, French, German and Belgian zoological gardens.

Ironically, the animal's luck abroad was reversed at home as one misfortune after another befell it. The first happened in 1894 when the Yongding River flooded and breached the wall of the hunting park, allowing a large number of David's deer and other game to escape, only to be eaten by hungry refugees. Then, in 1900, when the Eight-Power Allied Forces invaded Peking and marched through the hunting park, they killed all the remaining David's deer in the park. Thus at the beginning of the 20th century all *sibuxiang* in China had been annihilated.

Fortunately, 18 David's deer remained in European zoos, thus preserving a slim chance of survival for this rare and precious animal.

At that time there was an English duke (the Duke of Bedford) who was very fond of animals. With the aim to preserve this species, he spent large sums to buy all 18 deer, shipping them back to England and setting them free on his estate, Woburn Abbey. Woburn Abbey has lakes, swamp, trees, grassland — natural conditions comparable to those of Nanhaizi Hunting Park — so it was not difficult for the deer far from home to adapt to the new environment and breed. Moreover, in this new home they could safely endure the severe trial of two world wars. Nevertheless, war put a heavy mental burden on the duke, who feared that if the deer herd were destroyed by war, he would have to face the severe blame of the world's people. Abandoning his old idea of keeping the deer solely in his own hand and never disposing of any to others, he decided to distribute a few out of his herd of several hundred to some European and American zoos for safekeeping and exhibition.

Wanderers Returning to the Motherland

By courtesy of the London

Young David's deer

Zoological Society, two pairs of David's deer were presented to the China Zoological Society in 1956 to be exhibited at the Beijing Zoo. After an absence of over half a century the return of these "wanderers" enabled Chinese to see their *sibuxiang* once more.

It was inappropriate, however, to keep David's deer in zoological gardens, because they were accustomed to an active and free life. If fenced in, they would not breed well, the percentage of dystocia ranking first among all kinds of deer. Hence, owing to difficult labor, sterility, sickness and injury, the David's deer all came to an end by 1973. In December of that year the London Zoological Society again sent two pairs to China, but there were more cases of dystocia in the following years, so that by 1982 fewer than ten survived. There were demands both at home and abroad to build a new home for the deer returned to China. They

had become a "natural relic" in whom older Chinese found consolation and from whom younger Chinese received patriotic education.

Representatives from different circles were enthusiastic to take on the task of choosing a suitable locality for building a new home. Finally they decided on the old Nanhaizi site, rebuilt into Nanyuan State Farm, to reconstruct a deer park with an area of 66.66 hectares.

Through more negotiations Marquis Tavistok, new owner of Woburn Abbey, acting according to his father's will, promised to transport a group of breeders to China by air free of charge. Accordingly, a first batch of 22 David's deer landed at Nanhaizi in August 1985. Their return recalled the old story of how David had discovered the Nanhaizi deer herd 120 years before and how the herd had been destroyed by gunfire 85 years before.

Now their descendants had returned to their homeland and

fulfiled the wish of building a new home.

But that wasn't all. To promote its international wetland project, WWF sent another 39 David's deer from England to China in 1986 and set them free in a newly established reserve in Dafeng County in northern Jiangsu Province near the seacoast. This was another trial of "back to nature." The herd sent back to Nanhaizi from England in 1985 have multiplied in the place long inhabited by their ancestors. Their population has increased from a few dozen to more than 300, so that a few could be distributed to other localities.

David's deer has been designated as a first-grade national protected animal by the Chinese government, but there are no really wild David's deer in China. Those living at Nanhaizi and Dafeng County are semidomesticated. It is necessary to wait another score of years before those living in the reserves develop into truly wild animals.

A male David's deer

Other Deer Species Endemic to China

The deer family (*Cervidae*) has 17 genera and 38 species. Of these, ten genera and 18 species have been found in China. China, however, besides David's deer, has a number of endemic species.

White-lipped Deer

In the genus *Cervus* the white-lipped deer (*Cervus albirostris*), found only on the Qinghai-Tibet Plateau, is a first-grade national protected animal and very well known abroad. Many foreign zoological gardens are eager to obtain it, but so far only Nepal and Sri Lanka have received a few.

The deer has the highest habitat in the world, in summer reaching 4,850 meters. Its most outstanding characteristic is the pure-white patches on its upper and lower lips and throat, hence it is called white-lipped deer, but it has other local names, such as

The deer are fond of water, not only keeping themselves in water for long periods in summer, but often standing motionless in water even in cold winter. Young does like to chase and play in deep water, while stags are fond of bathing in muddy water, often throwing mud on their own back with their antlers.

Gestation lasts as long as nine and a half months, the longest of all species of deer. Most of the young are born in April or May, but some may be as late as September or October.

Most deer species are fond of eating twigs and leaves, but not David's deer, which mainly eat green grass, sometimes adding water plants. They are quite indifferent to twigs and leaves and do not gnaw bark or break off branches, thus they do not harm trees. In winter they are fed on hay and bran.

Two male and a female white-lipped deer in Qinghai Province

A lone male wapiti on a snow-capped mountain

yellow deer, rock deer and grass deer. Its antlers are also peculiar, making it very easy to distinguish it from other deer species. The antlers may reach 120 centimeters and are of a light color (sometimes white). They usually have five, at most seven, tines.

Its body is slightly smaller than that of the wapiti, with a shoulder height of 1.25 to 1.30 meters and a body length of 2 to 2.15 meters, but a tail length of only about 10 centimeters, the shortest tail among large deer. It may weigh 130 to 140 kilograms.

Its coat is yellowish brown in summer and brownish in winter, with a deeper blackish brown on the head and neck. It also has a light-yellow rump disk. The stiff hairs on the neck and foreback of males often grow in a reverse direction, looking like a wrinkled collar.

Morphologically, there are two points worth noting: The eye sockets are especially big, almost twice as large as the wapiti's, and the hooves are especially big and solid, good for mountain climbing.

Wapiti and Sika

Since wapiti (*C. elaphus*) and sika (*C. nippon*) are found in both China and foreign countries, they cannot be regarded as endemic to China, but these two species have many subspecies, some found only in China.

The Chinese wapiti is a large deer midway between the American wapiti and the European stag. Deer specialists count eight subspecies, of which I shall introduce some that have greater international fame and are generally hard to find.

Tianshan wapiti (*C. e. songaricus*) has the biggest body and antlers and is therefore regarded by hunters and specimen collectors of different countries as a most valuable deer subspecies.

According to international hunting records, the biggest Tianshan wapiti had a body weight of 380 kilograms, far excelling that of all wapiti subspecies found in Europe and Asia, but slightly inferior to the American wapiti. Tianshan wapiti antlers preserved in museums have a record length of 152.4 centimeters, a circumference of 21.6 centimeters and a spatial width of 177.8 centimeters, also far excelling records held by all species of wapitis in Europe and Asia.

The color of this subspecies is chiefly gray, deeper on the neck,

shoulders, limbs and lower body, with more orange on its rump disk and a black midline on its back and tail.

The Tianshan wapiti is principally found in the Ili River valley north of the Tian Mountains, from counties of Huocheng to Balikun. Despite its large population, this wapiti has rarely been exhibited by zoological gardens in China and abroad.

The Yarkant wapiti (*C. e. yarkandensis*), also known as Tarim wapiti, is found along the Yarkant and Tarim rivers to the Peacock River in southern Xinjiang. It is one of the very few deer that have not yet been exhibited by any zoo in China or a foreign country. Its morphological peculiarities include a big, distinct rump disk, a reddish color, and forward-leaning upper antlers. Its habitat is often between reed marshland and bush grassland, where it is concealed.

Changdu wapiti (*C. e.*

Sika deer

macneilli), also called white-rumped deer and well known in foreign countries by the name of white deer, is pale gray. Previously it was recognized as an independent species.

Despite hearsay that it is already extinct, some can still be found in western Sichuan and eastern Tibet in forests along the Jinsha, Lancang and Yalong rivers. The 1990 IUCN Red Book of Threatened Animals designated it as an I-class endangered animal.

In southern Tibet another subspecies (*C. e. wallichi*), widely

investigation, some still live in Yadong and Qusum counties and known as shou deer in Europe and America, is found on the southern slopes of the Himalayas.

Its coat is reddish brown and its rump disk yellow. Both body and antlers are very large. Each antler has five to seven tines. The longest on record is 141.6 centimeters, with a circumference of 16.5 centimeters.

Since zoological gardens of different countries have failed to get any in recent years, rumors circulated that it was already extinct, but some still live

in the mountain forests along the middle reaches of the Yarlung Tsangpo River. The shou deer has been provided with special protection internationally. The IUCN Red Book has designated it as an E-class endangered animal.

The sika deer (*Cervus nippon*) is simply called deer in Chinese, because it represents deer to the Chinese. This is probably because this species of deer is most commonly seen in China and also the best looking, with a mild temperament. In addition, it has the longest history in captivity, so it is the most beloved by the people.

Sika deer are also found in Japan, Korea and Vietnam, but China has the greatest numbers and the best known in the world. It has five subspecies, found in both south and north China. Unfortunately, after centuries of hunting, its wild population has nearly been reduced to zilch. Most of the subspecies are endangered or even nonexistent.

C. n. mandarinus (north China

Sika deer in the wild

subspecies), originally found in eastern Hebei and former Jehol provinces, became extinct in the last years of the Qing Dynasty, but a samll number of semiwild descendants are still kept in Chengde, a tourist resort.

C. n. hortulorum (Northeast China subspecies), largest of the sika subspecies, with a shoulder height of up to 110 centimeters and a weight of 120 kilograms, originally widely found in Jilin and Heilongjiang provinces, now has only a few small populations in the Changbai Mountains in Jilin Province.

C. n. kopschi (south China subspecies) was for a long time the most widely distributed deer in south and east China, ranging from Jiangsu and Zhejiang to northern Guangdong provinces, but things have changed a great deal in recent years. Hunting for its velvet has eliminated its populations from most of their previous habitats during the past few decades, so that many people fear it may already be extinct, but

reliable information confirms that some remaining populations still live in the mountains of southern Anhui and northern Jiangxi provinces. For instance, there are definitely more than a hundred in the Taohong Mountains in Pengze County of Jiangxi Province, where a reserve was established for the south China sika deer.

Lastly, there is also a subspecies (*C. n. Taiouanus*) in Taiwan. It is the smallest of the sika, with a shoulder height of only 80 to 90 centimeters. It also has the smallest population among the subspecies. It's doubtful whether any are still living in the wild, and probably only a few are left in zoological gardens.

Despite all these unfortunate conditions, there is also heartening information, i.e., the discovery of a new subspecies.

Between the mid-1960s and the early 1970s a population of some 100 to 200 sika deer was discovered at Ruorgai in northern Sichuan Province and in the Sichuan-Gansu border region.

These newly discovered Sichuan sika deer were given the subspecific name of *C. n. sichuanicus*. So far the subspecies has not been exhibited by any zoo in China or abroad, hence it is one of the most rarely seen animals in existence. Discovery of this subspecies has not only scientific value, but also great practical value, since it is useful

A small family of Hainan slope deer (or Eld's deer)

for improving the breed of domestic sika deer, which are widely kept in China, their total numbers far exceeding 10,000 and expected to increase.

The Hainan slope deer, or *polu*, is better known internationally as Eld's deer (*Cervus eldi*) or brow-antlered deer.

The antlers are quite different from those of wapiti and sika, chiefly because of the very nicely shaped brow tine.As for the body's general build, it closely resembles the sika's.

The Hainan slope deer is a subspecies (*C. eldi hainanus*) of Eld's deer, which has other subspecies in Myanmar and Thailand. In China it is found only on Hainan. Since it has a restricted range and small population, it is a first-grade national protected animal and an endangered animal in the international Red Book.

In fact it was once gravely endangered in China, for its population on Hainan had dropped from the original nearly 1,000 in the early 1950s to only 10 to 20 in the late 1970s. Thanks to timely and effective action for its protection, with two reserves established in Dongfang and Baisha counties, the remaining populations were saved. By the end of the 1980s the subspecies' numbers had increased to 100 to 200. The crisis of extinction was thus relieved. This deer is also an E-class endangered animal in the international Red Book.

Muntjak and Musk Deer — Chinese Miniature Deer

China has many endemic species of small deer. For instance, it has three endemic species in the genus *Muntiacus*. The Chinese muntjak (or Reeves' muntjak, *M. reevesii*), widely distributed in many provinces in east, south and southwest China, has been introduced by foreign countries in large numbers, especially by Britain where it has become a very popular game animal.

The black, or hairy-fronted, muntjak (*M. crinifrons*) was little known before 1949. From 1885 to 1920 only three specimens had been collected from two counties, Ningpo and Tonglu, hence it was recognized as the "most rarely seen" deer in the world, and its distribution range was erroneously believed to be limited to a small mountainous region in western Zhejiang Province.

Black muntjak with a yellowish head

However, recent investigations have shown it has a range far larger than previously believed, including a number of counties in western Zhejiang, southern Anhui and northeastern Jiangxi provinces. Some people estimate its population at 10,000, but even if this is so, it is still a very rare and precious animal. Living specimens have never been exported, and only two or three zoological gardens in China have exhibited it. It has been designated as a first-grade national protected animal.

A similar animal is the tufted deer (*Elaphodus cephalophus*), with three subspecies found in southwest China, southeast China

Male Chinese muntjak

and the Sichuan-Hubei border region.

Though not so rare as the black muntjak, it is nevertheless a rare animal endemic to China and is well known internationally. Up to 1980 only a few had been exported, often mistaken as black muntjaks, because they very much resemble each other. Both are black or blackish brown, have comparatively long tails and short horns, tufted hair on the crown, and, for the males, tusks. The only difference is one has black tufted hair and the other, yellowish.

China has one other species of small deer, the renowned river deer (*Hydropotes inermis*), commonly called *zhang* or *yazhang* (tusked deer) in Chinese, because it has no antlers, but is armed with long tusks. In

foreign countries it has long been known as Chinese river deer in international hunting circles. For many years foreigners coming to China to hunt were most zealous about hunting the river deer. For this reason it has been introduced to western European countries in large numbers. Formerly it was believed that this deer was found only in China south of the Yangtze River, but another population with very small numbers was recently found in Democratic People's Republic of Korea.

The river deer has some ecological peculiarities. First, it has the highest reproductive ability. While most deer produce one or two fawns per litter, the river deer may produce three to six, and they develop rapidly, reaching maturity in six months and capable of mating the same year. Next is its great ability to conceal itself and adapt to all sorts of environments, especifically it can not only conceal itself in reeds on riverbanks or small

Musk deer

islands, but also live on hillsides or farmland, in thick grass in graveyards or burrows in wilderness.

It can even live in the suburbs of densely populated cities along the middle and lower reaches of the Yangtze River, such as Nanjing, Suzhou, Wuxi and Zhenjiang. It is said that river deer introduced to foreign countries do likewise.

However, heavy hunting in recent years has reduced its range and numbers in China, so it was designated as a second-grade national protected animal in 1987.

Another group of small deer are the musk deer, whose general appearance closely resembles that of the muntjaks, especially the river deer. However, since they have a number of morphological and structural peculiarities, they are grouped into a special subfamily, the Moschinae. Some scholars, chiefly Chinese deer specialists, advocate separating the Moschinae from the Cervidae and setting up a family of their

own, the Moschidae. The deer's chief peculiarities include: Both male and female musk deer are antlerless, while all other deer, except the river deer, have antlers. The musk deer have a gall bladder, which is absent from all other deer. In addition, the male musk deer has a musk gland, which is an umbilical gland of secretion, generally called perfume sachet. The musk produced from this sachet is a valuable Chinese drug and is used as essence to produce the most costly perfume for international markets.

Concerning classification of the musk deer, different scholars have different views. Traditionally it was believed there was only one species of musk deer, that is, the northern

musk deer (*Moschus moschiferus*), but later views counted three or four species. According to Chinese scholars, China has at least four species. The northern musk deer is found in Xinjiang, Inner Mongolia, north and northeast China. The horse musk deer (*M. sifanicus*) is found in northwest and southwest China and Tibet. The forest musk deer (*M. berezowskii*) is found in the provinces of Hunan, Hubei and Guangdong and in Guangxi Zhuang Autonomous Region. The Tibet musk deer (*M. chrysogaster*) is found in southern Tibet and Nepal. In order to protect the musk deer, all species are designated as second-grade national protected animals.

Alpine Animals

A group of male argali in Qinghai mountains at Dulan

The many great mountain ranges in western China—Tian, Altay, Kunlun, Himalaya, etc. —are famous all over the world, not only for their great altitude and might, but also for the alpine animals living on them.

Argali—Biggest Wild Sheep in the World

Wild sheep have altogether four or five species, found in Asia, Europe and North America, including Asia's argali and urial (or sha), Europe's mouflon and America's bighorn and white sheep. All have big thick curved horns, but argali has the biggest body and most magnificent horns.

Argali consists of seven or eight subspecies, distributed in Kazakhstan, Mongolia and China's Inner Mongolia, Xinjiang, Qinghai and Tibet. Because its horns are particularly big, it is also known as big-headed sheep in its Chinese native haunts. Its huge body has won it the name Asiatic giant wild sheep internationally.

According to hunting records, a big male argali has a shoulder height of 115 to 120 centimeters and a body length of 150 to 175 centimeters. Its weight is 120 to 130 kilograms, with a few up to 150 to 160 kilograms. Females are much smaller, with a weight generally less than 80 kilograms. The longest horn on record is 157.5 centimeters, with a circumference of 54.6 centimeters.

A male argali

Female horns are short and straight.

The sheep is pale brown or grayish brown on the upper body, white or milky white on the lower body, with a dark stripe on the back. The rump is white or has a milky yellow rump disk. The throat and neck of male sheep have a white mane; the older, the more white hair.

Subspecies differ in body size, deeper or lighter color of coat, thickness and length of horns.

A subspecies (*Ovis ammon polii*), found on the Pamir Plateau between China and Russia, is known as Marco Polo sheep, because it was introduced by Marco Polo, the famous traveler, in his travel notes.

The horns of Marco Polo sheep, though not so big and thick, are exceedingly long, forming a great circle, with a world record length of 190.5 centimeters; hence it is regarded as a most precious trophy.

Argalis in western China mostly stay in alpine grassy marshland or shrub land 3,000 to 4,000 meters above sea level. In summer adult male sheep may climb to bare rocky regions over 5,000 meters above sea level, coming down only during the rutting season in autumn and returning to the flock to join the struggle for mating.

The males clash with all their might. Fortunately, their solid skulls are strong enough to protect their brains from fatal injury. They continue their clashing until one of them withdraws; otherwise he would be tossed out of the arena and dropped into a deep ravine.

In winter the flock has to combat heavy storms and trek through vast wilderness, moving from one peak to another in search of food.

During the long trek some sheep drop dead from hunger or exhaustion. Another danger is attacks from wolf packs, often resulting in a number of females and young falling victim. As for the big male sheep, although they are strong and powerful, they are also very tired, because their horns are too big and heavy, requiring too much energy to carry them over many miles. When wolves come near, they are too tired to run away; instead they lie down, using their horns as defenses. Travelers occasionally discover argali horns in the mountain wilderness of Qinghai and Tibet, the scars of wolf bites discernible.

Bharal—Another Kind of Wild Sheep

Outwardly a bharal resembles an argali, and since their distribution ranges overlap, hunters often mix them up.

Bharal on a Qinghai mountain

Actually they have only a distant relationship, belonging to different species and genus. Morphologically, the bharal stands midway between the sheep (*Ovis*) and the goat (*Capra*), so it belongs to a genus (*Pseudois*) of its own, which consists of two species, the typical bharal (*P. nayaur*) and the dwarf bharal (*P. schaeferi*).

The bharal is generally called blue sheep in foreign publications, as its body is mainly bluish gray, but it has patches of blackish-brown hair on its face and chest. Males also have black stripes on the front of their limbs and both flanks.

Bharal horns are olive green and comparatively smooth.

Though not so big as the argali's, they look big in comparison to their bodies. International big-game records indicate that the largest bharal horns come mainly from central and western Tibet. The longest on record is 84.4 centimeters, with a circumference of 34.3 centimeters, obtained from Gyaze, western Tibet.

A male bharal from the Min Mountains in Gansu Province has a shoulder height of 89.5 centimeters, a body length of 122.3 centimeters, a tail length of 20.5 centimeters, and a weight of 60 to 70 kilograms. These dimensions represent the upper limit of this species of sheep. A dwarf bharal seven or eight years old weighs only 28 to 30 kilograms. The dwarf bharal is a new species discovered in 1937 in Xikang (now part of western Sichuan). Although some scholars regarded it as only an individual variety, it was recognized in 1963 as a subspecies (*P. n. schaeferi*) of the typical bharal and in 1977 as an independent species (*P. schaeferi*).

The bharal population is noticeably greater than the argali's. It is not difficult to observe large groups of bharals on the northern slopes of the Himalayas, the Kunlun Mountains, the Jishi Mountains of Qinghai Province and the Qilian and Min mountains of Gansu Province. Despite reports of heavy hunting in recent years, bharal populations are still far from endangered. Foreign countries have shown concern over their safety, chiefly because bharals are very rarely seen in foreign zoological gardens. Although the zoos are very anxious to obtain a few of this

A herd of bharal on a mountain in eastern Tibet

species of sheep for exhibition, they apparently have had difficulty doing so.

Both argali and bharal are designated by China as national protected animals.

Bharals are true alpine animals, dwelling on high cliffs above the timber line in summer and winter and only occasionally entering forests. They gather in groups in spring and autumn, sometimes as many as 100 to 200 in a single group, but old males leave in summer to live a solitary life on peaks as high as 3,500 to 6,000 meters, often appearing on grassy slopes or bare rocky peaks. For this reason they are also called *shiyang* (stone sheep) or *yayang* (cliff sheep) in Chinese and are regarded as one of the highest mountain climbers among mammals.

Ibex

Ibex may be regarded as the most outstanding and most typical high mountain animal in the world. If a mountain climbing competition were to be held among all the high mountain animals of the world, the championship would undoubtedly go to the ibex.

In order to get out of the reach of snow leopards or other mountain carnivores, ibexes always choose to live on the most perilous peaks. With unclimbable cliffs on both sides and glaciers behind, they are quite safe from attack from the side or above.

Flocks of ibexes, under the leadership of an old male, usually begin seeking food in early dawn, but before they move, they wait for their leader to climb to the top of the peak for 10 to 15 minutes of surveying. Only after he gives the signal indicating all is safe and well in the surrounding area do they start seeking food. At feeding times a female ibex stands sentry.

The ibex has excellent sight, hearing and smell, making it very difficult to hunt it.

The ibex also boasts a pair of attractive horns good for making a trophy. The shape of its horn is quite different from the argali's and bharal's. It is not circular, but somewhat like a curved sword. Though not so big and heavy as the horn of the argali, it is big and long enough to satisfy any trophy hunter. The longest and biggest horns come from the Tian Mountains of Xinjiang—a world record of 147.3

Male ibex with big horns

centimeters. The horn is not round, but somewhat triangular in cross section, with a circumference of generally 25 to 30 centimeters at its base.

The ibex is not classified as a sheep, but as a species of goat, belonging to the genus *Capra*, whose typical species is *C. ibex*, consisting of a number of subspecies found in Asia and Europe. China has two subspecies: Tianshan (*C. i. almasyi*) and Altay (*C. i. altaica*). Both have bigger horns and bodies than other subspecies found in Central Asian, West Asian and European countries. A Chinese male ibex has a shoulder height of 101 to 107 centimeters and a weight of 90 to 93

kilograms.

All these alpine sheep and goats (argali, bharal, ibex) found in the high mountains of western China are rare and precious animals with high academic, artistic and economic value. They are often exhibited in leading zoological gardens and natural history museums. More scientific research on these animals is needed.

Wild Cattle and Antelopes

Wild yak is a rare and precious species very hard to obtain. Only a few wild yaks are in Chinese zoological gardens, whereas foreign zoos have only domesticated yaks.

Wild yaks are found only in China. Their native haunts are high, perilous and far away,

Male wild yak running in the wild

Big herd of wild yak on migration

making it difficult to capture and transport them. Their center of distribution is the eastern part of the north Tibetan Plateau, then north to the Austen Mountains and the western section of the Qilian Mountains; south to the north bank of the Yarlung Tsangpo River; east to the Jishi Mountains in Qinghai Province and Garze in western Sichuan Province; west to the Karakorum Mountains in the Tibet-Kashmir border region. Herds of wild yaks are chiefly found in the high mountains of Tibet, Qinghai and Gansu.

Wild yaks are typical Central Asian high mountain and plateau animals. They move to regions over 5,000 to 6,000 meters above sea level in summer and no lower than 3,000 meters even in winter. Despite bitterly cold winds and a ground covered by ice and snow, the wild yak, wrapped in long, thick hair, especially on the chest and abdomen, can lie on the frozen ground for a long time without being frostbitten.

The wild yak survives the long winter months by eating very poor, coarse grass and withered leaves and twigs, quenching its thirst with snow and ice. It may thus rightly be regarded as a "heroic" animal, the most cold resistant, hunger resistant, thirst resistant and hardship resistant of all animals.

The wild yak is physically much larger, stronger and more powerful than a domestic yak. A male wild yak has a shoulder height of 1.65 to 1.85 meters (a few may reach two meters) and a body length of 2.40 to 2.80 meters. In comparison, the shoulder height of a domestic yak is only 1.40 to 1.45 meters. The wild yak has a very big, bushy tail 90 to 100 centimeters long, with long hair both above and below. This type of tail is unique among all kinds of cattle. The body hair is dark brown all over, deeper in summer, lightly mixed with some yellow hair in winter, with some reddish-brown hair on the back. The tail is completely black. A small patch of dirty white appears on the lips.

The wild yak weighs 500 to 600 kilograms, the domestic yak under 300 kilograms.

The wild yak's horns are large, thick and curly, with both tips pointing inward toward each

A wild lone bull yak in northern Tibet

other, which is advantageous for use as weapons.

The horn of a wild yak bull is 60 to 70 centimeters long, with a record length of 97 centimeters. The general circumference is 35 to 40 centimeters, with a record thickness of 45.7 centimeters. The cows' horns are much smaller and thinner, but sharp enough to cope with a wolf attack.

Wild yaks are highly gregarious. Ordinarily they gather groups of 10 to 30 or more, but when new grass grows in spring and when they are migrating northward in summer, very large groups of 100 to 200 may be observed.

Old males, however, are solitary in habit, often leaving the herd to return only during the rutting season, which begins in late autumn.

Documentary statements alleging that wild yaks give birth in April when the grass turns green are incorrect. Records kept by the Beijing Zoo for one male and two females indicate that wild yaks usually mate in November and give birth to calves in late August and early September. Whereas documentary statements said sexual maturity came at 24 to 30 months, zoo records showed that calves born in 1973 were not yet fully mature sexually in 1976. Indications are that the documentary statements were made upon the observation of domestic yaks, for wild yaks are found only in China, and no foreign zoo has ever kept any wild yak.

Takin

Looking roughly like an ox, the takin has a basic morphology midway between sheep and cattle; therefore it belongs to the Ovibovini (Sheep-Ox) in classification, but its common names in its native haunts are *yeniu* (wild ox), *shanniu* (mountain ox) or *bainiu* (white ox), and it has a formal Chinese name of *lingniu* (antelope ox), all connected with ox just because it looks so like the ox.

Takin (*Budorcas taxicolor*) has a total of four subspecies, one each in Myanmar and Bhutan, but all in China, with much greater populations than the other two countries.

A few of the Chinese Sichuan subspecies (*B. t. tibetana*) and Shaanxi Qinling subspecies (*B. t. bedfordi*) were sent to foreign countries for exhibition in the 1980s, thus becoming the rarest and most precious animals in

Male takin at the foot of a mountain

An adult male takin kept by the Beijing Zoo has a shoulder height of 134 centimeters, a body length of 213 centimeters, and a weight of 189 kilograms. Very big males may weigh over 300 kilograms.

The horns part from the center of the crown, first bending to both sides, then curving to the rear, with the tips pointing slightly to the interior. Horns of old animals are rather blunt. A record 63.5-centimeter horn was obtained from the Himalayas.

Body color is so variable that it is difficult to denote subspecies based on color. Not only do different subspecies have different colors, but male, female, old and young of the same subspecies, sometimes even different individuals of the same age, have a deeper or lighter color. Only the Qinling subspecies (*bedfordi*) is yellowish all over, from light yellow to orange yellow, shining like gold in the sunshine. However, too, it has variations, in that the female

their zoological gardens.

The Qinling subspecies is best known in China and abroad under the name of golden takin. Animals found on Taibai Mountain in particular have long shiny golden hair all over their body without a single hair of a different color, looking very charming. Others found in the Qinling in southern Gansu Province are also draped in golden hair, but there is a small patch of blackish hair on the snout, hence they are sometimes regarded as a different subspecies.

Takin has a clumsy body, both the body and limbs sturdy and thick, a big head, thick nape, wide muzzle and fat nose; the limbs are short, the hooves big, resulting in an awkward, clumsy gait.

Golden takin

A pair of golden takin in Shaanxi Province

and younger animals are lighter in color, sometimes giving a silvery impression under the sunlight, hence called "big white sheep" by the country folks.

Distribution of the species is centered in the western China plateaus, going southward to the northwestern part of Yunnan Province and the extreme southern part of Sichuan Province and northward to the southern parts of Gansu and Shaanxi provinces; the eastern limit ends at the middle section of the Qin Mountains (Qinling) and the western limit ends at the eastern part of Bhutan, then turns northward to the vicinity of Pomi in Tibet.

The typical subspecies (*taxicolor*), also known as Himalaya subspecies, is distributed partly in Myanmar and Assam, then to the east it is found in the Hengduan Mountains in southeastern Tibet and northwestern Yunnan and also in the Gaoligong Mountains on the Yunnan-Myanmar border.

Takin usually stay at higher altitudes about 2,600 to 4,400 meters above sea level. They are also highly gregarious animals. Large herds consisting of some dozens or even a few hundred often gather in summer months, but usually become smaller in

A male serow at Beijing Zoo

winter months, because it's more difficult to find food then.

Habitually, herds stay in the forest in the daytime, coming out to seek food in early morning or evening.

Food includes fresh grass, shrub leaves and twigs, and tender branches of birch in summer, and bamboo plants, willow branches and elm bark in winter. Takin are particularly fond of licking salt in all seasons.

Takin are first-grade national protected animals. Only two foreign zoos keep five heads of takin. Qinling golden-haired takin were estimated to number about 1,300 in 1981.

Serow

In tropical and subtropical areas serow is one of few alpine and subalpine animals, highly renowned both in China and abroad. It is called *lieling* (maned antelope) or *sumenling* (Sumatran antelope) in China, but it has many common names, because it is widely distributed. For instance, it is called *mingzong yang* (white-maned goat) in Hunan and Hubei provinces, *yalu* (cliff donkey), *shanlu* (mountain donkey) or *shanluo* (mountain mule) in Sichuan and Yunnan provinces, *yeniu* (wild ox) in Tibet Autonomous Region, *tianma* (sky horse) in Anhui Province.

Besides south and southeast China, serow is found in Southeast Asian countries such as Malaysia, Thailand, Bangladesh and Sumatra in Indonesia.

As an alpine and subalpine animal, serow generally inhabits heights around 2,000 to 4,000 meters above sea level. It is an excellent mountain climber and leaper, acquiring the nickname "sky horse" because it often appears on high peaks, racing and leaping nimbly among very steep and precipitous cliffs.

Food is usually sought at dawn or dusk, when four or five animals move about in creeks or under the shadow of precipices.

The rutting season occurs in autumn (August to September) or winter (November to December) or even as late as early spring of the next year. Males challenge each other furiously for winning a mate. The females are pregnant for seven or eight months and often deliver their young (one or two per litter) between May and July. Sexual maturity arrives 20 to 22 months later.

The taxonomic position of serow is between the goat and the antelope, hence it is classified as the tribe Rupicaprini and genus

Capricornis, which consists of two species: the common serow (*C. sumatraensis*) and the smaller Japanese-Taiwan serow (*C. crispus*).

The common serow somewhat resembles a donkey, mule, ox, horse or goat, its size close to that of a donkey, that is, shoulder height 90 to 105 centimeters, body length 130 to 170 centimeters, tail length 9 to 12 centimeters and weight 100 to 140 kilograms. Both its ears and mane are very long. The species found in Taiwan, however, is much smaller, its shoulder height only 50 to 60 centimeters, body length 80 to 90 centimeters and weight only 20 kilograms. It has no mane.

Both male and female serows have horns, which are quite simple—slightly curved, with a few black rings and very sharp points. Length is 22 to 26 centimeters, the longest on record 32.4 centimeters, and circumference 13 to 16 centimeters. Body hair is mainly black, mixed with some grayish-brown and reddish-brown hair; the mane is grayish white mixed with some brown and black hair. Some individuals have a completely white mane, hence are called white-mane serow.

Serows in China belong to three subspecies, found respectively in the southwestern and southeastern provinces and the Great Snow Mountains in Lijiang County of Yunnan Province. Habitat of the Lijiang subspecies attains a height of 4,000 meters, so that serows living there have grown very long hair to resist the cold. Young serows with their mothers can lie on the snowy ground for hours.

Owing to geographical reasons (habitats too remote and mountains too perilous), the populations have suffered less from hunting, and are comparatively more numerous in Jiangxi, Anhui, Sichuan and Yunnan provinces.

The condition of the Taiwan serow is worth grave concern, however. Widely distributed all over the island a score of years ago, it has now become an endangered species as a result of poaching and deforestation. By the late 1970s and early 1980s only a few specimens could be captured occasionally, just enough to confirm that it was not yet extinct. Statistics from 1990 show fewer than twenty in captivity in zoological gardens—four in Taipei and eleven in Japan. It has been designated as a first-grade national protected animal.

Goral

Goral is usually branded as a goat-antelope, because its classification is midway between a goat and an antelope, just like the serow.

Some taxonomists claim it evolved from the serow or else both of them share a common ancestry.

The goral is slightly smaller than a serow, and the two can easily be confused. The ways to distinguish them are, first, serows have neck manes, while gorals are maneless; second, gorals have a throat spot, but serows haven't; third, serows have longer horns. Since gorals look more like a goat, their common names in China are mostly connected with the goat.

such as wild goat, blue goat, gray goat and mountain goat.

Subspecies differ slightly in body shape, size and sexual distinction. Generally they have a shoulder height of 64 to 72 centimeters, a body length of 120 to 130 centimeters and a weight of 28 to 35 kilograms. Both male and female have horns that are black, sharply pointed, smooth

above and wrinkled below. The average length is between 16 and 19 centimeters, with a record length of 23.2 centimeters.

The body is generally grayish brown or deep brown mixed with black and yellow hair. All individuals have a light-colored spot on the throat and a blackish-brown stripe on the back. Subspecies differ in body color, size, color of throat spot, and tail length.

Chinese gorals include four subspecies: The southeast subspecies (*Naemorhedus goral armouxianus*) is found in the provinces of Zhejiang, Fujian and Guangdong and in Guangxi Zhuang Autonomous Region; the southwest subspecies (*N. g. Griseus*) is found in Sichuan and Yunnan provinces; the northern subspecies (*N. g. caudatus*) is found in the provinces of Hebei, Shanxi, Shaanxi and northern Sichuan, and the Inner Mongolia Autonomous Region, and Beijing's outskirts; the northeast subspecies (*N. g. raddeanus*) is

Red goral in Tibet

Red goral in Tibet

found in Jilin and Heilongjiang provinces.

Gorals are mountainous animals, but not truly alpine animals. Their habitat are far lower than those of the alpine animals described above. Their safety comes not from height, but from perilousness. In fact, their habitats are no less perilous than those in high mountains, and their climbing ability is not inferior to that of true alpine animals.

Gorals usually live alone or in pairs; only rarely do they gather in small groups.

The animal has long hair and fine wool to withstand the cold. In winter it suns itself by lying on a rock, but it's afraid of hot weather, in summer hiding most of the time in some shadow, motionless, very difficult to discover.

Rutting season is in September and October, with a gestation of 240 to 260 days. One or two young are delivered in May or June.

Gorals are listed as second-grade national protected animals, and they are included in annex I of CITES (Convention on International Trade in Endangered Species of Wild Fauna) as an animal internationally prohibited from selling and purchasing.

Red Goral

For many years people believed that gorals had only one species with several subspecies. Then in 1961 a new species, the red goral, was officially named (*Naemorhedus cranbrookei*).

Despite its late acknowledgment, it was discovered as early as 1912 when an English officer, by the name of Bailey, reported that during his travels in southeastern Tibet he had observed some Tibetans wearing fur coats the color of red fox but said to be made from goral fur. Then in 1931 another Englishman, named Cranbrook, shot one specimen in the Adong River valley on the Tibetan-Myanmar border. He presented it to the British Museum, but it wasn't examined until 1960, when someone sent in a red goral pelt asking for examination, and it was finally recognized as a new species (*N. cranbrookei*). Specialists found out later that this new species was the same as *N. g. baileyi*, a

A chiru (or Tibetan antelope) running fast

subspecies of goral named in the 1930s for an animal discovered in Pomi in Tibet.

Whether it is a new species or a new subspecies, it is certainly one of the rarest of animals. Although the definite number of wild populations is not yet known, only three zoological gardens, in China (Shanghai) and foreign countries (Myanmar and the United States), keep a small number of red goral.

Investigations by specialists of the Shanghai Zoo from 1979 to 1983 showed the distribution range of red gorals in Tibet included the counties of Pomi, Linzhi, Motuo, Milin, and Dalang to the west, Chayu to the east and up to the Sino-Myanmar and Sino-Indian borders to the south.

Ecological habitats of the red goral are chiefly restricted to thick primeval forests, mostly at altitudes between 2,000 and 4,500 meters above sea level, where temperatures are mild and rainfall is abundant.

Red gorals are expert climbers,

able to climb vertical precipices very rapidly when facing danger. They also make vertical migrations in different seasons, climbing to the mountain grassland above the timber line in summer and going down to the mixed forests or shrub land in winter. Food consists mainly of pine creeper, lichen and tender leaves and twigs of shrubs.

Males live a solitary life outside the mating season, while females live with the young. Mating mostly occurs in December and delivery occurs in June.

Chiru

Chiru is the Tibetan name of this animal; its Chinese name is

zangling (Tibetan antelope). It is also called *orongo* in Tibet. Its scientific name is *Pantholops hodgsoni*.

Strictly speaking, this animal, found on the Qinghai-Tibet Plateau, is not an alpine animal, because it is not skilful at climbing high peaks and steep precipices. Nevertheless, its habitat is very high, sometimes as high as that of the wild goats. For instance, chirus on the north Tibetan Plateau usually go around 4,000 to 5,000 meters, sometimes up to 6,000 meters, but these are not precipitous high mountains; it is vast, desolate prairie. Chirus are more correctly called plateau animals than alpine animals. Chirus are rare and precious

Chiru in northern Tibet

animals not because they are few in number, since, in fact, they are as numerous as wild sheep, but because they are so difficult to capture that no zoological garden in the world has ever kept or exhibited one.

The chiru's native haunt is remote, communication is inconvenient, and the animal itself is a remarkable runner. Despite the thin atmosphere on the high plateau, the animal can run as fast as 80 kilometers an hour. This is not only because it is so light and nimble, but also because its muzzle is particularly swollen and it has many air sacs in its nostrils, aiding its breathing.

A group of chiru on the move

55

A Northeast China tiger looking for food

Carnivorous Beasts

Carnivorous beasts principally belong to the three families, Felidae, Ursidae and Canidae. The majority are concentrated in Felidae.

Tiger

The tiger is not only the largest, most beautiful and most ferocious species among all carnivorous animals, but also a wild animal that maintains close relations with human beings and possesses high economic and ecological value.

India considers the tiger its national animal. Although China has no national animal in name, the tiger is its de facto national animal. The Chinese have called it the king of animals since ancient days, and people often place the tiger and dragon on equal terms.

While the dragon is an imaginary supernatural beast and often represents a king or an emperor, the tiger is real in existence and is often used to symbolize military power, dignity, prowess and tactical excellence,

A family of Northeast China tigers

hence the symbol of an outstanding commander, general or athlete.

The tiger has had an age-old influence on Chinese civilization. Innumerable paintings, sculptures, poems, folk songs, and other works have taken the tiger as their subject. It is mainly because the tiger has had such a close and profound relationship with our civilization that the Chinese think so highly of it.

Even though the tiger is a menace (sometimes a serious menace) to livestock and even to human safety, it is classified as a protected animal. It is regarded as a first-grade national protected animal not only in China, but in almost all tiger-producing countries. Many non-tiger-producing countries have also listed it as a key internationally protected animal, strictly forbidding not only

hunting and capturing, but also the purchase or sale of any product made from its body.

Even though the total number of tigers in China is not so large as in India, China ranks first in the world as to the number of tiger subspecies and the area of tiger distribution. That's why the condition of Chinese tigers is always taken seriously by the whole world.

Tigers are found only in Asia

and have only one species (*Panthera tigris*), but this is divided into nine subspecies according to differences in body size, color, density of stripes, thickness of fur and thickness of tail.

Of the different subspecies the Bengal tiger (*P. t. tigris*) is found in China, Myanmar, Pakistan, Bangladesh; the Indo-Chinese tiger (*P. t. corbetti*) is found in China, Myanmar, Malaysia, Thailand and the three Indo-chinese countries; the Javan tiger (*P. t. sondaica*), Bali tiger (*P. t. balica*) and Sumatran tiger (*P. t. sumatrae*) were all originally found in Indonesia; the south China tiger (*P. t. amoyensis*) is found only in China; the northeast China tiger (*P. t. altaica*) is found in China, Russia and Korea; the Chinese Turkestan tiger (*P. t. lecoqi*) was originally found in China's Xinjiang, and the Caspian tiger (*P. t. virgata*) was originally found in the former Soviet Union, Iran, and Turkey.

Four of the above-mentioned tiger subspecies, namely, the Javan, Bali, Chinese Turkestan and Caspian tiger, are already extinct. Five remain. The most numerous is the Bengal tiger, whose number jumped from 1,800 in 1973 to the present 4,000 to 5,000 as a result of the Project Tiger, executed by

Hiding in the trees

the Indian government.

Next is the Southeast Asian (or Indo-Chinese) tiger, whose number in the mid-1980s was estimated at no fewer than 2,000. The Sumatran tiger comes in third with a population of 800 to 1,000.

As for the northeast China tiger, although very few are left in China and Korea, more remain in Russia, so that the total number is estimated at more than 300.

Least numerous is the south China tiger, an endemic subspecies in China, with 30 to 40 in the wild and about the same number in zoological gardens.

The tigers' characteristics differ according to the different habitats. Some people claim tigers in the south are more vicious and include more man-eaters. Superficially, this sounds somewhat reasonable. For instance, the Bengal tigers are fiercer than the northeast China tigers and have more man-eaters among them, while the south China tigers take an intermediate position between the two. But

A Northeast China tiger drinking at a mountain spring

59

why? Is it the influence of geography or climate? After careful analysis scientists concluded it had nothing to do with climatic or geographic elements.

Fundamentally it is the result of local faunal conditions, especially the difficulty or ease of obtaining food, and also the local social environment. It seems that the farther south, the greater the density of human population and the more complicated the influence. It gets more difficult to obtain food, and the struggle is intensified. All these elements combined have toughened the tigers physically and their temper may have eventually turned them into man-eaters. But after all, the percentage of man-eaters among tiger populations is always very small, not only in China, but also in India—less than

one in ten thousand. Thus despite the existence of man-eating tigers, almost all tiger-producing countries designate the tiger as a protected animal.

As for the wild northeast China tiger, over 200 live in Russia's far eastern area, fewer than 30 in the D.P.R. of Korea, and others in Jilin and Heilongjiang provinces in northeastern China. That's why the northeast China tiger is also known as the Siberian tiger, Manchurian tiger, Amur tiger and korean tiger.

But whether in Russia, Korea or China, the distribution range of the northeast China tiger has gradually been contracting. Before 1930 there were tigers in both the Greater and Lesser Hinggan mountain ranges in northeastern China and also in

the mountains across the Sino-Russian border.

In the 1930s and 1940s, as a result of overhunting and deforestation, tigers in the Greater and Lesser Hinggans were continually driven eastward until they became extinct.

In the early 1950s zoological gardens in Beijing and some provinces collected more than 100 young tigers and killed a number of adults from forest centers in the Lesser Hinggans Mountains and also in the Wanda Mountains in eastern Heilongjiang Province and in eastern Jilin Province.

Even though hunting and capture were forbidden later on, the number of the tiger stock was drastically reduced. Tigers disappeared from the Lesser Hinggans by the 1960s. By the mid-1970s the tigers of Heilongjiang Province had retreated to the Wanda Mountains on the Sino-Russian border, and the tigers of Jilin Province had retreated to the Sino-Korean border.

Leopard, Snow Leopard and Clouded Leopard

The leopard, though not so rare as the tiger, is nevertheless a large carnivorous beast of high economic and exhibition value. The fact that it is being endangered merits serious attention.

Leopard

The common Chinese name for the leopard is golden-coin leopard. In different localities it is called silver-coin leopard, plum-flower leopard, and giraffe leopard, depending on body color and spot patterns.

Since leopards have such a wide distribution, there are many varieties and native haunts, with slight difference as to size, color and pattern, forming different subspecies. According to studies made by specialists in carnivore, leopard subspecies in Asia and Africa total more than 20. China has at least three. Classification of Chinese leopards has been rather rough. It seems that not even the international leopard studbook is precisely accurate on this question, chiefly because of insufficient data and reference materials on Chinese leopards. A divergence of views on the morphology, range and even scientific names of the south, north and northeast China leopard that started in the 1930s continues even now.

The traditional view regarded the northeast leopard as *Panthera pardus orientalis*, with a range consisting of northeast China, the D.P.R. of Korea and the Ussurian region of Russia; the north China leopard as *P. p. fontanierii*, with a range consisting of Beijing, Hebei, Shanxi, Inner Mongolia, northern Shaanxi, Gansu, Qinghai and northern Sichuan; the south China leopard as *P. p. fuscus*, with a range consisting of central China (Henan, Hubei, Hunan, Jiangxi), east China (Zhejiang, Fujian, Anhui), south China (Guangdong, Guangxi), southwest China (Yunnan, Guizhou, Sichuan) and some Southeast Asian areas.

A lot of views changed later on. Some people said that the leopards in Jilin, Liaoning and Korea were actually subspecies of the north China leopard; the real northeast leopard could be found only in northern Heilongjiang and the Ussurian region of Russia.

As for the north China leopard, some people recognized *P. p. japonensis* as its accurate scientific name, adding that since Japan did

Golden-coin leopard

not have leopards, this specimen was actually from Beijing, therefore really belonged to the north China leopard. In addition, the name *japonensis* was given five years earlier than *fontanierii*, so logically it should be acknowledged as the formal name.

Moreover, in recent years some scholars have not only acknowledged *japonensis*, but moved a step further, widening its applicable range from north China to central and east China, including some populations originally recognized as south China leopards. The 1990 edition of the international leopard studbook even referred to *P. p. japonensis* as "Chinese leopard," indicating international circles go so far as to regard the north and south China leopard as one subspecies.

All these confusions may be attributed to the fact that all Chinese leopards exhibited by zoological gardens of different countries are without clarified origin, thus resulting in the confusing of their native haunts with their subspecies.

However, our own view is that the morphological differences between leopards from north China and leopards from south China are quite clear. The former have longer hair (winter length about four centimeters) of light yellowish color. The ring pattern is also lightly colored and not so distinct. The latter have short hair (winter hair on back two to three centimeters long) of a deep orange color, with ring pattern darker, deeper and very distinct.

Leopards from the northeast look more like a north China leopard than a south China leopard. The winter pelt has thick, fine wool and more milky-white hair. As for body size the three subspecies differ little.

The male Chinese leopard has a body length of 1.25 to 1.30 meters, a tail length of 85 to 90 centimeters, and a weight of 50 to 60 kilograms, at most under 80 kilograms. The female weighs only 36 to 45 kilograms.

Leopards are far more numerous than tigers, thanks to their greater adaptability and concealment and a much wider range of food. Birds, monkeys and other small animals, often hunted

Snow leopard on a mountain slope

by leopards, are seldom eaten by tigers. Therefore places without tigers often have leopards. For instance, there are no tigers on the Xikang-Tibet Plateau or in the hilly regions of Hebei and northern Shaanxi, but leopards may be found there. Chinese provinces without any leopards are limited to Shandong, Jiangsu, Taiwan and Hainan.

Of the three subspecies, south China leopards rank first numerically. Next come the north China leopards. The smallest number is the northeast China leopard. Whether in northeast China, Russia or the D.P.R. of Korea, it is hard to find them. According to cat family specialists, the northeast leopard may be regarded as one of the rarest and most endangered members of the cat family, on a par with the south China tiger.

Snow Leopard

The second species of leopard in China is the snow leopard (*Panthera uncia*), popularly known as *aiye bao* (mugwort-leaf leopard) or *tu bao* (native leopard). It belongs to the same genus as the leopard, but not the same species. It closely resembles the leopard in morphology and body size, differing chiefly in color, which is generally much lighter than the leopard's. It is almost pure white on its upper body, with many black spots and irregular black circles on the upper body and limbs, but not the lower body. Its tail also has spots and circles above, but is pure white

without any spots below. All the spots and circles are comparatively indistinct (especially in winter) or far less distinct than the leopard's. The morphological characteristic of the snow leopard is its very long, thick tail rich with long hair. Its coat of long hair makes it look bigger than the leopard, but actually it is a little smaller, seldom weighing over 55 kilograms, with a body length of 105 to 120 centimeters and a tail length of 90 to 100 centimeters.

Snow leopard is a typical animal of the Central Asian plateaus and high mountains. The Qinghai-Tibet Plateau is its center of distribution, reaching the Himalayas in the south and

Altay Mountains in the north, and to the limits of western Sichuan Province and southern Gansu Province in the east. Almost half of western China, including most of the famous high mountains in Xinjiang, Tibet, Qinghai and Gansu, are native haunts of the snow leopard. Although other countries, such as India, Pakistan, Afghanistan, Mongolia and Russia, all have snow leopards, their area of distribution and total populations are not so large as China's. However, the snow leopard is a very solitary animal, hence the density of its population is especially thin. A very large area of distribution may not yield very large numbers of animals. That's why it is a rare and precious animal.

From its name we understand the snow leopard inhabits areas above the snow line in high mountains. Unless compelled by necessity, it never goes below the timber line. According to investigation, snow leopards in the western Himalayas often climb to a height of 5,500 meters in summer; only when the summit is covered with deep snow in winter and no food can be found there does it move down. Its heavy coat protects it from cold or wind. It moves up and down the mountain in different seasons in search of wild game and other food. Besides various ibexes, bharals, argalis and musk deer living in the high mountains, the snow leopard hunts domestic goats and sheep grazing in high mountains during the warmer seasons. When the herds move down in winter it follows them down.

When winter is over and the grass returns, small game, such as marmots, pikas and ground squirrels, living high up the mountain, emerge from their caves. Then the snow leopard also returns to the high cliffs. Its camouflage coat of bluish gray and indistinct spots and circles makes it very hard to distinguish it from the rocks or snow drifts where it hides.

The hunting tactic of snow leopards is basically the same as the leopard's, i.e., a matter of ambushes and surprise attacks by lying on big rocks and waiting for any game passing below. Generally they avoid attacking a male ibex, bharal or argali with big horns, preferring female or young animals.

Snow leopards are in heat from January to March, with a gestation of 98 to 105 days. A litter of usually two or three is born in May or June. Births may occur every year in a zoo, but are said to occur every other year in the wild. Males are capable of mating as late as 15 years old and are estimated to live 17 to 19 years.

Internationally, the snow leopard has been designated as an E-class endangered animal by the Red Book, the same as the tiger. An organization by the name of International Snow Leopard Trust (ISLT) plans to hold a symposium every two years in snow leopard countries. Such a symposium was

Clouded leopard on a tree

held at Xining, Qinghai Province, in 1992, when delegates from various nations expressed great concern about the problem of conservation of snow leopards in Qinghai. This has become a serious problem. More than 200 snow leopards have been killed or captured by poachers in the last 30 years.

Clouded Leopard

Morphologically, the clouded leopard closely resembles the leopard, but is markedly smaller than the leopard, snow leopard and tiger, hence may be regarded as a medium-sized carnivorous beast.

Its body pattern has given it the following popular names in China: *wuyun bao* (dark clouded leopard), *guike bao* (tortoiseshell leopard), *heye bao* (lotus-leaf leopard). It has several cloud-shaped or tortoiseshell-shaped spots and black stripes on both flanks in addition to many black spots on the head and limbs. There are also six longitudinal stripes on the neck. Its coat is a mixture of grayish-yellow, charred-tea and black hairs.

Compared to the other leopards, its limbs are shorter and tail is longer. The ratio between body length and tail length is almost 1:1, or a body length of 90 to 110 centimeters and a tail length of 80 to 95 centimeters. The tail is long and thick with 12 to 14 blackish-brown rings.

A clouded leopard weighs 15 to 20 kilograms. Males are much bigger than females.

The most outstanding characteristic of the clouded leopard is not body shape, however, but dental shape. Its upper canines are particularly big, so big that some scholars have been reminded of the saber-toothed tiger, extinct long, long ago. If you compare the skull of a leopard and the skull of a clouded leopard, you will find the former much bigger than the latter, but the canines of both skulls are almost of the same length. For this reason, taxonomists designated another genus (*Neofelis*) for the clouded leopard. It is not in the same genus (*Panthera*) as the other large cats, such as lion, tiger and leopard.

The two genera have another morphological difference in that

the structure of hyoid and ligament in the pharynx and larynx sector enables the larger carnivorous beasts to swallow large lumps of meat and roar with great volume, but allows the smaller carnivores to swallow only small lumps of meat and scream in a shrill voice. Therefore despite its name of clouded leopard, it is not included in Pantherinae (subfamily of leopards), but in Felinae (subfamily of cats).

The clouded leopard is basically an animal of the Oriental Region, distributed to Borneo and Sumatra in the south. Its northern boundary is the Qin Mountains in Shaanxi and Gansu. It is also found in Taiwan.

Although it has a wide distribution range in Southeast Asia, its populations are very small in most countries except China, with the typical subspecies (*Neofelis nebulosa nebulosa*) found in many Chinese provinces, including the provinces of Zhejiang, Anhui, Fujian, Jiangxi, Hunan, Guangdong, Hainan, Yunnan, Sichuan, Shaanxi and Gansu, and Guangxi Zhuang Autonomous Region. The Taiwan animal had been recognized as another subspecies, *N.n. brachyurus*, or short-tailed clouded leopard, until later examination confirmed that its tail was not short, therefore it belonged to the same subspecies as the continental animal.

Clouded leopards in tropical and subtropical regions usually inhabit thick jungles and hunt mainly monkeys, birds and arboreous rodents. But since these animals are not very abundant in the Chinese temperate zone, the leopards have changed their hunting range. Besides hares and wild rats, they hunt smaller ungulates, such as muntjaks and gorals. Occasionally, under pressure of hunger, they venture into villages to raid poultry and small livestock. Though a vicious animal, it dares not attack human beings under ordinary conditions. There have been no reports of its killing or eating any human being.

The clouded leopard has two reproduction seasons in a year, March to April and July to August. The ones kept in zoological gardens may bear two litters a year, mostly in March and June. Each litter has two to four cubs, each weighing 150 to 180 grams at birth, changing color gradually from black to yellow. The leopard can climb a tree as early as six weeks. It has a life span of 16 to 17 years.

The clouded leopard is regarded as a second-grade national protected animal. The international Red Book designates it as a V-class endangered animal.

Giants in the Thick Forests

Two of China's largest land mammals are found in her tropical and subtropical primeval forests—the Asiatic elephant and the gaur. Typically, they belong to South and Southeast Asian tropical regions. In China they are found only in the forests of southern and southwestern Yunnan.

Since they have a very high scientific and economic value, are very limited in number and endangered, they have both been designated as first-grade national protected animals as well as E-class endangered animals in the international Red Book.

Asiatic Elephant —Second Largest in the World

Historically, Asiatic elephants have been in China for many hundreds or thousands of years. According to legend, they helped feudal lords cultivate the land, but how much or how little truth there is to those legends we do not know. What we do know is that the ancient Chinese learned about elephants through foreign tributes to the Chinese imperial court. Neighboring countries presented elephants to China as articles of tribute as late as the Ming (1368-1644) and Qing (1644-1911) dynasties. In addition, rulers of the minority ethnics in southern Yunnan had kept a number of elephants as domestic animals before the Chinese revolution of 1911; therefore Chinese people were not totally ignorant of the elephant—its huge size, queer shape, mighty power, intelligence, working ability, etc.

However, most Chinese,

A group of Asiatic elephants

before 1949, didn't know the elephant existed in China as a wild animal. They had no way to learn about it through the press or even textbooks, so they probably believed that wild elephants had become extinct in China long, long ago. They did not know that a small number remained in a remote corner of Yunnan, where no zoologist or journalist had ventured during the long years of civil war and the war against Japan.

Biological investigations began in these regions in the late 1950s and early 1960s. Elephant distribution in Yunnan was roughly understood after that.

In Xishuangbanna wild elephants chiefly live in Mengla County and Mengyang District. More were later found in three counties of Ximeng, Cangyuan and Yingjiang in western Yunnan near the Sino-Myanmar border.

According to more than a dozen investigations made in 1960-1968, there were 101 wild elephants in Xishuangbanna and 45 in western Yunnan. Later investigations increased the total number. For instance, in March 1985 the *People's Daily* reported that more than 230 wild elephants had been found in southwestern Yunnan. Another report in March 1986 said an additional 36 had been discovered in Niuluohe Nature Reserve, Simao County. Thus the wild elephant population in China totaled fewer than 300, including males, females, adults and young. This was obviously too small a number for so large a country as China, especially compared to countries such as India and Myanmar that possess thousands of wild elephants.

Making friends

In order to both conserve and increase the present elephant stock, Chinese wildlife conservation officials decided to tighten protective measures against poaching and deforestation, which occasionally took place in the elephants' native habitats. In addition, new nature reserves are being set up at such places as Mengla, Mengyang and Cangyuan. Chinese wild elephants are gradually, it seems, recovering from their endangered condition.

All Asian elephants belong to a single species, namely, *Elephas maximus,* which includes four subspecies. Besides the nominal subspecies (*E. maximus maximus*), found only in the eastern part of Sri Lanka, two other subspecies are found in Sumatra and Sri Lanka respectively. Elephants of all continental countries (India, Bangladesh, Myanmar, Thailand, Malaysia, Cambodia, Laos and Vietnam) belong to the same subspecies *(E. maximus indicus).* The elephants in Yunnan also belong to this subspecies.

As for the origin of the Yunnan wild elephants, there have been two opinions in the past. One suggested they were descendants of remnant Chinese elephants that had migrated from the central provinces. Owing to changes in natural (chiefly climatic) and social conditions (chiefly the increase in human population and economic development), the elephants were forced to move southward. Their populations became smaller and smaller, their ranges narrower and narrower, as they moved from the central provinces to east China and then to west China and finally to Yunnan, where they found refuge in the primeval forests of southern and southwestern Yunnan until the present time.

The other opinion is that they came sporadically from neighboring elephant producing countries, particularly from Myanmar, Laos and Thailand.

From historical, geographic and habitual aspects, the second suggestion is much more likely, since similar cases may still be found, whereas the likelihood of the first suggestion is actually very little.

First, the time when elephants were living in the central provinces is too remote. From inscriptions on bones or tortoise shell and from bronze elephant toys of the Shang Dynasty (16th-11th century B.C.) we may conclude that the time when elephants existed in the central provinces was several thousand years ago.

Second, the distance from the central provinces (chiefly Henan) to the southwest frontier is too great. Very likely the migrants would have been eliminated long before they reached their destination. In contrast, the Indo-Chinese forests are closely connected with the Yunnan forests, thus much easier to travel.

Asiatic elephants chiefly inhabit forests with more water resources. But forests are divided into two types: hot, damp rain forest at lower elevations and comparatively cool forest at higher elevations, sometimes up to 3,000 meters above sea level. According to observation, Yunnan elephant populations are mostly active on hillsides or in river valleys below 1,000 meters above sea level with the following basic elements: abundant food and water resources, sufficient shade and safe areas for retiring.

The elephants are fond of eating various juicy plants, such as bamboo leaves, wisteria, liana, green grass, tender twigs and leaves and wild fruits of all kinds. Each elephant may consume 200 to 300 kilograms of fresh food per day and in addition throw away an equal or greater amount. Thus unless the feeding ground is extremely rich in these plants, it is impossible to sustain a herd of elephants for a long time. For this reason, elephant herds have to move very often to find new feeding grounds. The feeding time is usually dawn or dusk.

When the sun is too strong, the elephants move to the shade of deep forests.

Elephants are gregarious animals with herds basically composed of families. The herd leader is usually a big, old female elephant of a family.

Smaller herds average eight to ten; larger herds, ten to twenty; yet very large herds, formed temporarily by a number of families, may number up to a hundred, in which case the leading female may have several other females serving as her assistants.

Every family has a big male tusker protecting the group. He does not necessarily mix with the group, but moves about alone, following the group at some distance. Once the family is threatened by danger, he immediately rushes ahead to defend it.

Elephants mature at 14 to 15 years, usually later in the wild than in a zoo, for wild life is far less leisurely than zoo life, where feeding is much better and easier.

There were two Burmese elephants living at the Beijing Zoo. The female delivered her first calf before fully 14 years old, which means she was pregnant at only 12, and the male elephant was a successful breeder at only 11. It was an especially precocious elephant that had its first mating with an Indian female elephant when only eight years old.

A small number of male Asiatic elephants, like this male Burmese elephant, are tuskless. Tuskless male elephants often develop particularly well with a long, thick and powerful trunk. Tusks are natural weapons of male elephants. Tuskless male elephants, using their particularly strong trunk as a weapon, sometimes even overwhelm a tusker that is physically not so strong. However, whereas big elephants may use their powerful trunk to punish weaker and smaller opponents, usually dare not use it as a weapon against a furious tiger.

An old Asiatic elephant living at Beijing Zoo

The trunk is an all-round tool that elephants use for eating, drinking, or picking things up. If it is very seriously wounded by the sharp claws or teeth of a tiger, the disabled elephant may suffer hunger and thirst. Knowing this, it raises its trunk high when confronting a tiger.

Elephants have no definite rutting season. Calves are usually born in late autumn, probably as a result of mating prior to the tropical rainy season.

The length of their gestation is also not definite, averaging 21 months, with the longest time 24 months and 13 days, and the shortest, only 17 months and 13 days. Generally a single calf is born; twins are rare.

Big males are often bad-tempered during the rutting season, so one must be careful not to approach them. Human casualties from elephant mischief in zoological gardens mostly happen in this period. Such elephants produce a foul-smelling overflow of oily fluid on both cheeks. Especially bad-tempered male elephants in the wild are called "rogue." Such elephants are much more dangerous than mischievous zoo animals, for they often create terror in villages by attacking villagers and destroying houses.

Fortunately, no such rogue elephant has been reported in Yunnan Province.

According to records over many years, the life span of an elephant is close to that of humans', i. e., 60 to 70 years. The longest on record is 99 years.

71

Gaur—White-limbed Wild Ox

Another species of giant wild beast found in the tropical forests of southern and western Yunnan is the gaur, a white-limbed wild ox simply called wild ox in many Chinese publications and even on the Chinese national protected animal list, which is obviously an improper name. Since there are many (more than a dozen at the least) species of wild oxen in the world, each with its special scientific name, it is certainly undesirable to name any of them simply wild ox.

Natives of Xishuangbanna call this wild ox *baiwazi*, or "white socks," in Chinese, because the lower section of its limbs is white. I prefer to rename it white-limbed wild ox.

Of all wild oxen this white-limbed wild ox, or gaur in English, is the largest, with shoulders often higher than 1.90 meters, some reaching 2 meters, and a body weight of over one ton, much greater than the largest wild yak.

Other characteristics of this ox include: (1) an especially high shoulder extending to the middle

Yunnan gaur

Yunnan gaur (white-limbed wild ox)

of its back, tending to make the animal look even taller and larger than its actual size; (2) a tail that is neither long (85 to 90 centimeters) nor thick; (3) a magnificent pair of horns on the bull, 70 to 75 centimeters long and 45 to 50 centimeters in circumference. The horns have big curves and sharp, widely spaced tips. The horns are largely olive green, but the tips are black.

As a species (*Bos gaurus*) it has several subspecies distributed in China, India, Bangladesh and Indo-Chinese countries.

The subspecies found in Xishuangbanna and western Yunnan forests is believed to be *Bos gaurus readi*.

A report published in 1986 said more than 600 of this giant wild ox were living in Xishuangbanna, so far only one female gaur is on exhibit in a Chinese zoo, so that the vast public has no opportunity to see how magnificent a wild bull can be.

Owing to its viciousness, attempts to domesticate the gaur have not so far succeeded, but a half-wild, half-domestic ox, called gayal, is found in the Gaoligong Mountains on the Yunnan-Myanmar border. It is said to be a hybrid descendant of the gaur and domestic ox and very possible to be domesticated in Dulong Nu Autonomous County, northern Yunnan Province.

Rare Treasures of the Steppe and Desert

The Junggar, Tarim, Turpan, and Qaidam basins and the Taklimakan Desert are renowned not only for their valuable minerals, but also for their many rare and precious animals.

The great northwest China is a vast expanse of plateau, mountain and basin, with deserts and semideserts. There we may find three species of particularly rare and precious ungulate animals: the world's only surviving wild horse; the wild ass, an animal that is neither horse nor donkey, but often called wild horse by the people; and the wild camel, ancestor of the two-humped domestic camel.

Wild horses and wild camels are endemic to the border region between China and Mongolia. Wild asses have two subspecies (or species). One (Mongolian wild ass) is found in northwest China and Mongolia, the other (Tibetan wild ass) in Tibet and Qinghai. Other subspecies are found in countries of Central and West Asia.

The conditions of these animals are quite different, but they are all rare and precious animals of the world. There is no longer any wild population of the wild horse. Wild asses, although still living in the wild, are extremely rare in zoos. Only a few wild camels are kept by Chinese zoos, and none by any foreign zoos.

In China they are designated as first-grade national protected animals. In other countries they are internationally recognized as endangered animals requiring special protection.

Wild Horse

The name wild horse may refer to the various extinct species of horse living in the wild in the past or specifically to the only species that is still living in the world, i.e., the Przewalski horse, or the Mongolian wild horse.

Since the typical specimen of this species was obtained from Chinese territory and since China and Mongolia are the only countries where remnant wild horses may still be collected, Chinese scholars and wildlife lovers are naturally more concerned and enthusiastic about the past and present conditions of the wild horse.

As a matter of fact, from 1878, when Przewalski discovered the wild horse in the Junggar Basin of Xinjiang, to 1980 this animal had never been exhibited in China, and no Chinese natural history museum had ever exhibited any specimen of a wild horse.

It was first exhibited in China in September 1980, when the Beijing Zoo exchanged a pair of wild asses for a pair of wild horses from the San Diego Zoo in the United States.

By the end of the 1980s some 120 zoological gardens of different countries, including China, were keeping more than 900 wild horses in captivity. All were descendants of a few dozen

A herd of wild horses

wild horses captured in the Kobdo area of western Mongolia at the turn of the century by a team dispatched by Carl Hagenbeck, boss of the world-famous Hagenbeck Circus. At that time wild horses in the wild were still plentiful, and capturing was still comparatively easy. However, transporting the female and young horses was a long, arduous job, since there were no railways or highways or motor vehicles in Mongolia and Siberia 80 or so years ago. It took more than 11 months for the caravan of wild and domestic horses (used as stepmothers for wild foals), mule carts and camels to go from Kobdo to Hamburg. Twenty-four of the 52 foals died midway, leaving only 28 to arrive

safely at Hagenbeck Zoo in Hamburg. All the wild horses kept by zoological gardens in the world today are descendants mainly of these 28 foals, plus a few more captured later by men of the Russian czars. If wild horses are really extinct in wilderness areas of Xinjiang and Mongolia autonomous regions, then the captive populations now kept by zoos will follow the example of David's deer and become real "treasures" of mankind.

As for differences between the wild horse, the domestic horse and the wild ass, the outward appearance of the wild horse is little different from that of the domestic horse. It is approximately the same size as

the Mongolian pony, with a shoulder height of 1.30 to 1.40 meters and a body length of 2 to 2.30 meters.

Only through close examination may one note the following differences: (1) The head and limbs of the wild horse are proportionately heavier and burlier. From the side, the head has a flatter contour. The oblique line from the forehead to the muzzle is less slanting. (2) The back of the wild horse is also flatter, with less prominent shoulders and rump. (3) The mane of the wild horse is short and always erect (unless the horse is sick or weak). It ends behind the crown, so that no frontal hair (indispensable to the domestic horse) can be seen. (4) Both the mane and the tail of the wild horse have short hair, which is absent from the domestic horse. Wild horses shed and regrow their manes and tails annually, whereas domestic horses do not. (5) It is comparatively easy to

Wild horse

Wild ass on the run

differentiate the three species of Equids from the forms of their tails. (a) The tail of the domestic horse has long hair from the base to the tip. (b) The tail of the wild horse has very short hair for 10 to 20 centimeters, then long black hair down to the end. (c) The tail of the wild ass has short hair except for a large brush of long hair at the end. (6) The ears of the wild ass, though shorter than donkey's, are much longer than the wild horse's (7) Both the wild horse and the wild ass have a black stripe down their back, but the former's is very narrow and inconspicuous in winter, while the latter's is broad and conspicuous in all seasons. (8) The lower limbs of the wild horse are obviously darker (sometimes nearly black) than the average color of the body, but the limbs of the wild ass are the same color above and below. However, the flanks of the wild horse are a uniform color above and below, whereas the flanks of the wild ass show a clear contrast between the upper and lower parts, with an obvious demarcation in the middle.

Wild horses and wild asses also differ in movement and behavior. Wild asses usually gather in groups. If startled, they quickly disperse, fleeing in all directions. Wild horses, however, always maintain a column formation. When the order to flee is given by the big stallion, the other horses form a single file, led by a young stallion, with foals in the middle and mares covering them in front and behind. The whole column is under the protection of the big stallion, which escorts it at either the head or the side, depending on conditions.

If a herd of wild horses is threatened by wolves, the big stallion also takes the lead in meeting the challenge, but wild

Mongolian wild ass

asses show no concern for each other when fleeing.

According to records kept by zoological gardens, the wild horse has a gestation of 320 to 343 days. The earliest age for mating is two, and the earliest age for delivery is three. The latest age for delivery is 23 to 24. The longest life span for wild horses is 33 years for males and 34 years for females. Adult wild horses weigh 200 to 350 kilograms and newborns 25 to 30 kilograms.

Wild Ass

The so-called wild ass is neither an ass nor a horse.

The wild ass found in Asia is also a different species from the African wild ass. The latter is the real wild ancestor of the domestic ass, while the former is not, for it lacks the shoulder and limb stripes of domestic asses. The ears are much shorter than a donkey's; the hooves are smaller than those of a horse, but bigger than those of a donkey. The call of a wild ass is like a horse's neigh, not like a donkey's bray. This gives Chinese country folk more reason to call it a wild horse instead of a wild ass.

As a species, the Asiatic wild ass has a much wider distribution than the wild horse.

Different subspecies of wild asses are found in a greater part of Central and West Asia, eastward to Jining and Shangdu of Inner Mongolia, westward to Syria and Iraq.

Two major subspecies (sometimes recognized as full species) of China are the Tibetan wild ass (*Equus hemionus kiang*) and the Mongolian wild ass (*E. h. hemionus*). The former is larger, with a shoulder height of 135 to 142 centimeters. A female may weigh 250 to 300 kilograms; a male, 400 kilograms. The color contrast on the flanks of the Tibetan wild ass is more conspicuous than on the Mongolian and other subspecies, with the upper part very red in summer or brownish in winter and the lower part, including throat, chest and abdomen, pure white.

The Mongolian wild ass has a shoulder height of 120 to 135 centimeters and a body length of 2 to 2.20 meters. The head is also smaller in proportion than the Tibetan wild ass's. Its mane is shorter and its color paler, grayish in winter and sandy-brown in summer. The color contrast on its flanks is also not so obvious,

77

Wild ass in Xinjiang

Mongolian wild ass

sometimes having no contrast at all.

Populations of both the Mongolian and Tibetan wild asses were previously very large. Before 1949 field observers had witnessed herds of up to 1,000 Mongolian wild asses in seasonal migrations. In the early 1950s travelers and road builders also saw herds of several hundred moving together at places in Qinghai and Xinjiang. Later on, the populations gradually decreased, owing chiefly to unrestricted hunting, but also to human pressure. Many moved from their native habitats to remote interior or border areas.

The ecological habitats of wild asses are much more complicated than the wild horse's, because they have such a wide distribution. They include not only prairie regions, such as in Qinghai and Xinjiang, but also high mountain regions, such as in Tibet, and desert regions, such as in Syria and Pakistan.

Tibetan wild asses are good mountain climbers, climbing to elevations of 4,000 to 5,000 meters. They usually like to inhabit vast prairies or deserts, because it's easier to escape from wolf packs in such locations. Once they are chased by wolves, however, they seek refuge in high mountains or hilly ravines.

The running speed of the wild ass, according to investigations made by motorist teams sent to Mongolia, may reach 64 kilometers an hour. Its endurance is also good, for it can run 40 to 50 kilometers without rest at an average speed of 48 kilometers per hour, which means that, under normal conditions, wolves are unable to catch them. The wild ass is fond of racing with motor vehicles, not only chasing after the vehicles, but running ahead. Unfortunately, this gives hunters a chance to shoot. Another unlucky trait is its curiosity. To satisfy this, it not only follows hunters wherever they go, but even approaches their camps to find out what's what.

Fortunately, very few hunters take advantage of this weakness, because, according to their standards, the wild ass is not a valuable hunting trophy, having no big horn or tusk or beautiful fur, therefore no legal position in international game contests.

Moreover, it is deeply hated by big game hunters, for their hunting plans are often spoiled by its curiosity. It very often tracks the hunters, but once its curiosity is satisfied, it bolts away with a big noise, thus revealing the presence of the hunters and startling other big game animals concealed

nearby. As a result, the game animals escape, and the hunters have wasted all their time and energy.

Wild Camel

The wild horse and wild ass are not wild ancestors of the domestic horse and domestic ass (or donkey), but the wild camel is definitely the ancestor of the domestic camel.

The birthplace of wild camels is the desert regions of Central Asia, and their limited range has been decreasing with time. It is now restricted to the southwestern part of Mongolia bordering on China's Inner Mongolia, Xinjiang and Gansu. Although accurate figures for the Mongolian population are unavailable, a rough estimate is 300 to 500. Some are known to make seasonal migrations every year.

As for wild camels in China, they have been observed or captured in Ejne Banner and Alxa Right Banner of Inner Mongolia, Dunhuang and Assay of Gansu, Annanba and Qaidam Basin of Qinghai, Yiwu, Hami, Turpan, Lop Nur and Ruoqiang of Xinjiang. These places united into a vast area of tens of thousands of square kilometers, which includes the Arjinshan Wild Camel Reserve (15,000 square kilometers), founded in 1988. The total number of wild camels in this area has been estimated at between 1,000 and 1,500.

The ecological habitat of wild camels is extremely harsh. Even animals with the greatest vitality, such as the wolf, can move about only in the outskirts of such a region and dare not live in its interior.

A nearly lifeless land, its temperature may reach 60 to 70 degrees centigrade in summer and minus 30 degrees centigrade in winter.

The mean annual rainfall is only 10 to 20 millimeters, and the evaporation rate is high, so even birds die of thirst. If a wild camel ventured out of the desert in search of food or water, it gave waiting wolves a chance to make a kill.

After many years of such rigorous trial, the wild camel basically adapted to the unfavorable conditions, undergoing a number of physiological or even structural modifications. For instance, its long fur protects against both fierce sunshine and heavy blizzard; its long, narrow nostrils and dense eyelashes efficiently prevent damage from sandstorms. It sweats and urinates little, thus prolonging resistance to thirst. Supplementary water may come from eating even very coarse plants. Under its soles a horny layer half a centimeter thick enables it to walk on broken, stony ground and hot, sandy ground with ease. Its long limbs and flat soles also enable it to run as fast as a horse, at a speed of 30 kilometers an hour for 60 kilometers nonstop.

Newborns can walk after two hours and can follow their mothers after 24 hours. Independence comes at one year and maturity at four to five years. The life span is 35 to 40 years.

Differences between a wild camel and a domestic camel are quite obvious. Generally the wild camel is leaner and taller than the domestic camel. Its limbs and neck are longer, its head is smaller and its muzzle is shorter. The skull of a wild camel is about 2.5 centimeters shorter than that of a domestic camel. Its ears are shorter, and its soles are smaller and narrower, the footprint only half as large as the domestic camel's. However, its toes and nails are longer.

The body hair of the wild camel is generally short, except on some parts of its neck and forelimbs; it is never so long and thick as the domestic animal's. The hair is a consistent yellowish brown.

The most important difference, however, is the humps. The humps of a wild camel are pyramid shaped, with a round base and a pointed end, and smaller than those of a domestic camel. Moreover, the humps of wild camels are thinly haired, with no drooping hair. In summer, after molting, the humps of domestic camels still have thick hair on top, whereas those of wild camels are entirely hairless. The humps of wild camels are also more solid, never drooping to one side.

All these morphological patterns of the wild camel are identified with their living conditions. For instance, their lean, tall bodies, long limbs, small, narrow soles, and solid, pointed humps are consequences of living in the wild. Wild camels do not need to carry burdens at a steady pace; instead they need to be able to run fast and be nimble and quick. They spend the greater part of their day laboriously seeking food and have no leisure to store fat in their humps.

Our zoological garden noticed two more differences: The wild camel ruminated longer and more often every day, and when it got angry, it didn't spit feces the way the domestic animal did, but kicked the keeper with its foreleg. Moreover, when it was in heat in the spring, it not only spit white foam from its mouth, but often got unruly, chasing and biting its target (a female domestic camel) and also the keeper.

Among so many zoological gardens in the world only two (Beijing and Lanzhou) keep wild camels. It is really one of the most rarely seen captive animals in both China and abroad.

Wild camel

Aquatic Mammals

Aquatic mammals may be divided into two big categories: those living in seas and oceans are known as marine mammals; those living in rivers and lakes are generally called aquatic mammals.

Chinese marine and aquatic mammals have two peculiarities: a great number of different varieties, but few endemic species.

China has a coastline of 18,000 kilometers, stretching from the Gulf of Tonkin in the south to Bohai in the north. Mammals belonging to the order Cetacea alone include more than 30 species of whales and dolphins, which include both the largest animal in the world, the blue whale, and the most ferocious animal in the world, the killer whale. Even though varieties of Chinese marine mammals are rich, the number of aquatic mammals endemic to China is extremely small, because the Chinese seas are located far from the two poles of the earth and

therefore lack such rare and precious birds and mammals as are endemic to arctic and antarctic regions. For instance, China has only three or four species of animals belonging to the order Pinnipedia (various sea lions, sea bears, sea leopards, walrus, or sea elephant) and only one species of animal belonging to the order Sirenia. Also, in spite of the large number of whales and dolphins, most are "travelers" between Chinese and foreign seas, and not endemic to China. The only aquatic mammal that may be counted as peculiar to China is the Yangtze dolphin, which is not a marine mammal, since it lives only in the Yangtze River and never swims out to sea. While only one species of marine mammal worth mentioning is the dugong. Though it is not strictly endemic to China, it is a rare and precious animal found in Chinese waters, for it consistently stays in the South China Sea and often appears in the coastal waters of Guangdong, Guangxi and Taiwan.

Yangtze Dolphin

This is a species of small toothed whale belonging to the family Platanistidae, which consists of several species of ancient and primitive small toothed whales found in the Ganges, Indus, Amazon, and Yangtze rivers and a few other rivers and lakes belonging to the Yangtze River system.

The Yangtze dolphin is the latest discovered (1916) and named (1918) of the toothed river dolphins and also the smallest in number and most endangered, hence generally regarded as one of the rarest and most precious of animals. It was designated as an E-class endangered animal by the international Red Book and a first-grade national protected animal in China.

The Yangtze dolphin is also known as the Chinese river dolphin and the white-finned dolphin. It is sometimes miscalled white-flag dolphin, because "flag" and "fin" are both

Yangtze dolphin (or white-finned dolphin)

pronounced *qi* in Chinese, so *baiqitun* may be translated either as white-finned dolphin or as white-flag dolphin. It also has a nickname in China—giant panda of the Yangtze River—that may reflect the general love for this aquatic mammal.

A major morphological characteristic of the Yangtze dolphin is its long, slender snout, which is different from the short, gradually pointed snouts of the different species of sea dolphins.

The snout of the Yangtze dolphin is about 40 centimeters long from its tip to the nostril. The jawbone is nearly 50 centimeters long, with 62 to 70 teeth in the upper jawbone and 60 to 70 teeth in the lower jawbone.

The body is streamlined, roughly like a sea dolphin's, with a length of 1.5 to 2.5 meters and a weight of 150 to 240 kilograms. It has a low triangular dorsal fin and a pair of palm-shaped pectoral fins. The caudal fin is flat, smooth and forked in the middle. The forehead is swollen like a round bump. The eyes are as small as beans and nearly blind. The ear holes are as tiny as pin points, so the hearing is also close to zero. The nostril is a porthole on the left side of the crown. The body is light gray on the back and pure white on the abdomen. The pectoral fins are light gray above and white below, hence the name of white-finned dolphin.

The distribution of the Yangtze dolphin was originally very wide, including not only the lower and middle reaches of the Yangtze River, from the river's mouth to the Three Gorges of Hubei-Sichuan provinces, but also the Qiantang and Fuchun rivers and Dongting and Poyang lakes. Since their numbers were large, they were not so difficult to see. However, with the continued development of river navigation, fishing and trawling in recent years and unrestricted hunting and capturing, accidental injury and killing were unavoidable. More than 20 were reported lost in 1984, leading naturally to a decrease in their populations. According to surveys by scientists of the Aquatic Biology Institute of Academia Sinica in the past few years, Yangtze dolphins no longer

Playing with water

appear in the lakes or branches of the Yangtze River, and there were only some 300 in 42 schools along a 1600-kilometer stretch of the Yangtze River from Taicang of Jiangsu Province to Yidu of Hubei Province in 1986. With these figures as the basis, they proposed establishing two sections of the Yangtze River (Honghu to Xintankou in Hubei Province, Anqing to Chengdezhou in Anhui Province) as dolphin conservation zones and setting up a natural breeding station at the city of Shishou in Hubei Province.

Yangtze dolphins generally live in deep sections of the Yangtze River and dislike getting near ships and riverbanks. They swim to shallow water only to catch small fish. They enter the big lakes in summer when the water level is high and return to the deep water of the Yangtze River to pass the winter.

They are gregarious animals, swimming in schools of at least three to five, usually eight to ten or as many as twelve to eighteen. They swim rather slowly, far more slowly than marine dolphins. Judging from their weak sight and slender snouts, they must often seek food in muddy water or even in the mud of river beds.

Its main food is the various varieties of river fish. Qiqi, a captive Yangtze dolphin, eats 9 to 10 kilograms of fresh fish every day. Although it has many teeth, it does not chew its food carefully, but swallows head and tail whole. Since it has strong digestive power, its excrement is crushed to putty.

The Yangtze dolphin is a warm-blooded animal with a constant temperature of about 36 degrees centigrade. Since the atmospheric and water temperatures of the Yangtze River are rather low in winter, it is assumed the Yangtze dolphin has an effective body temperature regulating system in addition to cold resistance power.

With its sight and hearing both degenerated, it depends upon a very sensitive sonar system for seeking food, avoiding enemies, chasing mates and making connections. By testing Qiqi's sonar system, Chinese acoustics specialists made out that the connecting signal of the Yangtze dolphin is a sort of whistle or scream roughly like the whistle of humans. The signal for pursuit and orientation is a sound like that of a clock. All are within an ultrasonic frequency range that has a sensitivity far superior to our artificial radar. As an eyeless, earless animal living in turbid river water, it depends upon this sonar system to maintain its existence.

Dugong

The Chinese name for this animal is a transliteration of its English name, dugong, but it is better known as the mermaid of the high seas.

The mermaid was both imaginary and substantial. For hundreds and thousands of years the enchanting beauty with a woman's body and a fish's tail had been known to countless people through innumerable stories, legends and tales. All these imaginary accounts had a common origin, the dugong.

As for its distribution, previous reports mostly concentrated on the tropical and subtropical Indian Ocean regions and very rarely referred to Chinese regions. This was chiefly because most of the tales about mermaids were related by ancient seamen, particularly those coming to Asia from Europe through the Red Sea and Indian Ocean. Although there were tales about "human fish" in ancient China, nothing was ever said about the dugong. As late as 1931 and 1955 specimens were obtained from the beaches of southern Taiwan and southern Guangxi respectively, finally confirming that the dugong lived in Chinese waters.

In appearance the dugong resembles whales, dolphins and elephants. It is thick skinned, shaped like a spindle, almost neckless, back round as a ball, forelimbs paddlelike, tail flat, one pair of udders on the inner side of the forelimbs and abdomen. All these closely resemble members of the order Cetacea (whales and dolphins).

Yet it also has morphological similarities to the order Proboscidea (elephants). At least three morphological structures indicate the earliest ancestors of the dugong and the elephant could have belonged to the same branch. (1) The upper incisors of the dugong (also the manatee) protrude from the muzzle like elephant tusks. (2) The structures of their cheek teeth are also similar. Only a few front cheek teeth are exposed for mastication, leaving all the rear cheek teeth buried in the jawbone as reserves, moving ahead slowly one after another to replace fallen old teeth. (3) Their hearts are similarly branched in the upper portion.

From this evidence it may be presumed that the earliest sirenians were terrestrial herbivores that became aquatic mammals probably during the Eocene epoch.

The dugong has a body length of 2.7 to 3.5 meters, circumference of 2 meters and weight of 350 to

500 kilograms. The largest may be over 4 meters long and weigh close to one ton.

The dugong is an animal of the tropical and subtropical estuary and shallow sea, submerging itself in the daytime and exposing itself at night. On warm sunny days, however, it may swim to the surface to sun itself.

Seaweed and other water plants in these regions are sufficient to supply its consumption, which averages 20 to 30 kilograms per day.

Unlike manatees, which can also live in freshwater inland rivers, dugongs can live only in sea water. They have better cold resistance, however, so they can feed and move about as usual even when water temperatures drop to six or seven degrees centigrade.

It's also not so active as the dolphin, swimming rather slowly and awkwardly at a speed of only two to five nautical miles an hour. While young dugongs swim with their front flippers, adults use their tails as propellers and their front flippers to modify the swimming direction and to crawl on the sea bed.

Dugongs emerge from the water every three to five or ten to twenty minutes to breathe.

Dugongs are gregarious animals. Smaller groups consist of eight to ten, larger groups of a few dozen. Large populations are apt to be seen around Weizhou Island and Xieyang Island off the southern coast of Guangxi Zhuang Autonomous Region, at anytime in the year. Fishermen of Beihai City used to hunt them in fishing boats before the 1970s. Dugongs were hunted chiefly for their fat for oil refining, in addition to the meat for eating and skin for processing hides. One animal can produce five to six gallons of refined oil.

Free hunting of dugongs has been prohibited since the animal was designated as a first-grade national protected animal by the government. It is also a V-class endangered animal in the international Red Book. Recently the Guangxi authorities decided to establish a conservation zone 380 kilometers long and 2,000 square kilometers in area off the coast of Hepu County.

Since it is an animal not adapted to freshwater, the dugong is difficult to keep and very rarely seen in zoological gardens. A few specimens kept by the Shanghai Zoo didn't live long. In other countries only one Japanese zoo had dugongs in 1990. The dugong's life span is estimated to be 40 years.

Rare Birds

Possessing the largest number of bird species in the world, China is fortunate in its "heavenly endowment."

Although China has only 7 percent of the world's total land area, it has more than 13 percent (1,186) of the world's total bird species.

The ratio of Chinese bird species to those of the former U.S.S.R. is 10:6 and to those of the U.S.A., 10:6.6. China even has more than the whole of Europe and the whole of North America. With such rich bird resources, China naturally has many rare and precious species, including not only particularly beautiful and glamorous birds, but also birds with high scientific, cultural and economic value.

In our limited space we can introduce only a small number of representative species, especially the cranes and pheasants, which are the elite of Chinese birds.

A pair of black-necked cranes singing happily

Chinese Cranes

Of the 15 species of cranes in the world, China has eight or nine, including some of the rarest and most precious. Cranes found in China include the red-crowned, Siberian white, common, black-necked, sarus, hooded, white-naped, demoiselle and sandhill. The sandhill crane (*Gruscanadensis*) is usually found in North America, but it was spotted in south China several years ago. It has not yet been determined whether or not it was simply a casual visitor.

As for the other species, all except the sarus crane, a South Asian species found only in Yunnan in China, are wide ranging. Some breed in northeast China and some in northwest China, but all are migratory birds. Six species breed in Zhalong Nature Reserve in Heilongjiang Province.

It was declared at an international crane conservation conference in Nanjing in February

1984 that there were more than 1,800 red-crowned, black-necked and Siberian white cranes in China, all these three species having the lead in the world.

Red-crowned Crane

Representative of Chinese cranes, the red-crowned crane often appears in Chinese poems and paintings. Since it is often painted with celestial beings and hermits, it is also called celestial crane. Painters give it a tall stature, long limbs, pure-white plumes, inky-black tail coverts, bright-red crown; it strides proudly with its chin up, expressing both arrogance and freedom.

Red-crowned cranes breed in northeastern Asia, a few in Russia and Hokkaido, Japan, but mainly in northeastern regions of China, especially the province of Heilongjiang. A general survey of wildlife resources in that province in 1975-1976 found a total of 1,300 red-crowned cranes.

The red-crowned crane is a first-grade national protected bird in China and a V-class endangered animal in the international Red Book.

It is a resident in Japan's Hokkaido, but a migrant in various parts of China and Russia, spending the winter months in the south and returning north in spring to breed.

Red-crowned cranes in northeast China mostly fly to Jiangsu and Anhui provinces to spend the winter on the seacoast or in peaceful, quiet locations on lakes and swamps. A survey of Jiangsu beaches in December 1982 counted 361 red-crowned cranes overwintering there.

With the aim of changing the crane from a migrant to a resident, Zhalong Nature Reserve in Heilongjiang Province organized a red-crowned crane domestication team. Newly hatched chicks were collected from the wild and small groups put under the care of a keeper, who trained them with a herding system. After 50 days of training he led them to the field and let them seek food by themselves. This continued for 85 to 90 days, then trial flying began. According to the rules, no matter how far they flew, once signal was given, they were to fly back to the base. Sometimes the chicks flew back with wild cranes accompanying them. In this way Zhalong Nature Reserve successfully

A lonely black-necked crane

domesticated a few dozen red-crowned cranes in a few years. Some were given to parks and zoos in other cities. The cranes no longer migrate in winter.

According to plan, the next step for Zhalong is artificial hatching, so that larger groups of domesticated cranes may be produced for scientific research, school education and public exhibition.

Red-crowned crane with her newly hatched chicks

Red-crowned cranes with chick

White Crane

The English name of this crane is Siberian white crane, because foreign ornithologists believed its breeding ground was limited to Siberia and the birds were only migrants or overwintering birds in China.

However, it is possible some migrant white cranes breed in northeast China in the course of flying north in spring from their wintering ground; although this has not been confirmed, flocks of some dozens of white cranes stayed at Zhalong for one week, and larger groups (90 to 120 birds) stayed longer (from early May to mid-May) in the vicinity of Lindian County, seeking food and resting. Twice birds were observed in the act of mating.

The highest count for the breeding cranes in Siberia had been 300, so the International Crane Foundation (ICF) had estimated the total population of white cranes in the world as 320. However, populations of white cranes overwintering along the lower reaches of the Yangtze River have been increasing since 1983, when a migrant bird nature reserve was established. By mid-February 1984 the number of white cranes concentrated at Poyang Lake had increased to 840. Nevertheless, international ornithologists still regard the white crane as the most endangered of all crane species.

In China both white cranes and red-crowned cranes are designated as first-grade national protected animals, but the international Red Book recognizes the red-crowned crane as a V-class endangered animal and the white crane as an E-class endangered animal,

White cranes on migration

Black-necked cranes with bar-headed geese

equivalent to the status of the American whooping crane, the rarest crane in the world.

White cranes and red-crowned cranes are closely similar in appearance, but the white crane is all white except for its primaries, giving it the name black-sleeved crane; it has no black feathers on its tail or neck. The white crane also has reddish legs, while those of the red-crowned crane are blackish. In addition, the white crane is larger.

Black-necked Crane

This crane is endemic to China, breeding and overwintering within Chinese territory. Since its native habitat is remote and its population very small, it is rarer even than the white crane. Up to the mid-1980s not a single foreign zoo had exhibited this crane. ICF headquarters in Wisconsin, well known for its collection of cranes from all over the world, had no black-necked crane until 1988,

when it finally acquired one from China. By 1990 outside China only the ICF in Wisconsin and the Berlin Zoo had black-necked cranes.

In general black-necked cranes breed on the Qinghai-Tibet Plateau and overwinter on the Yunnan-Guizhou Plateau. It is the only high-plateau crane in the world. According to investigation, its main breeding localities include Angren and Gar in Tibet and Yushu in Qinghai Province, and its main overwintering localities include Zhaotong and Zhongdian in Yunnan Province and Weining in Guizhou Province.

The outer appearance of the black-necked crane is also largely similar to that of the red-crowned crane, but its neck is not half black, half white, but wholly black, and its tail feathers are also black, not white like the red-crowned crane's.

Black-necked cranes calling to the sky

Chinese Pheasants

To the world's ornithologists China has always been the "kingdom of the pheasants."

China has 56 of the 276 species of pheasants in the world, or one-fifth of the total number. Furthermore, Chinese pheasants include many of the world's most renowned, most splendid and outstanding species, the majority of which are special to China.

Golden and Copper Pheasants

We should like to introduce the golden pheasant (*Chrysologphus pictus*) and the copper pheasant (*Chrysolophus amherstiae*) first, because they have been the best known among people for many years. The Chinese copper pheasant is also known abroad as Lady Amherst's pheasant. It is simply unbelievable that nature could compose such wonderful creations perfectly blending bright red, golden yellow, sky blue, jade green, pale gray, orange, brown, black and white on the body of one bird. It is all the more amazing to discover that both birds have that many colors yet in completely different patterns, as if painted by two great masters.

Both these beautiful pheasants are designated as second-grade protected animals, because they are widely distributed, found in many places in southwest and central China, and have large populations. In addition, large numbers are kept by zoological gardens, and they reproduce easily. According to statistics compiled by the *International Zoo Yearbook*, 62 zoological gardens in different countries bred 563 golden pheasants in

Golden pheasant

Copper pheasant (or Lady Amherst's pheasant)

Elliot's pheasant (or white-neck long-tailed pheasant)

it has long been a valuable exhibit in Chinese and foreign zoos. In order to conserve it, the state elevated its protection from second to first grade.

The Chinese name for Reeves's pheasant is white-crowned long-tailed pheasant. Another species of Chinese long-tailed pheasant, known in Chinese as the white-necked long-tailed

1989, and 29 zoological gardens bred 256 copper pheasants in the same year. Although the pheasants are still "precious," they are no longer very "rare."

Long-tailed Pheasants

All pheasants have long tails, but the genus *Syrmaticus* was specially named for long-tailed pheasants and includes several highly reputed rare and precious species.

The longest tail belongs to Reeves's pheasant (*S. reevesii*), a species endemic to China. It not only has an especially long tail, but also is very handsome, so that

Reeves's pheasant (or white-crowned long-tailed pheasant)

pheasant, is Elliot's pheasant (*S. ellioti*). This pheasant, found in east and south China, also belongs to the first-grade national protected animals and E-class endangered animals in the international Red Book. A third species is the black-necked long-tailed pheasant, or Mrs. Hume's pheasant (*S. humiae*), also a first-grade national protected animal, found in Yunnan Province. A species found in Taiwan, known as the black long-tailed pheasant, or Mikado pheasant (*S. mikado*), is a first-grade national protected animal and a V-class endangered animal in the international Red Book. There was a rumor several years ago that it was already extinct, but a few have been found in the past one or two years. It is regarded as one of the rarest and most precious animals of Taiwan.

Besides the long-tailed pheasants, there are several species of tragopans (or horned pheasants) and monal pheasants worth introducing.

The yellow-bellied tragopan (*Tragopan caboti*) is the most interesting. Being the first-grade national protected animal and

E-class endangered animal in the international Red Book, this bird, endemic to China, is found in south China, especially Fujian Province, hence it is often called Fujian tragopan. It is rarely seen outside China. Only a few specimens are exhibited in American zoos. This bird is particularly renowned for its courtship performance. Almost all pheasants are skilful courtship dancers, but the performance by the yellow-belled tragopan is particularly attractive as it displays itself energetically but comically before its beloved and a crowd of spectators. Several other species of tragopans are found in Tibet, namely, the crimson-bellied tragopan (*T. temminckii*), the gray-bellied tragopan (*T. blythii*), the black-headed, or western tragopan (*T. melanocephalus*) and the satyr tragopan (*T. satyra*), each with its own special features.

As for the monals, Chinese call them rainbow pheasants, because their bodies have a metallic radiance. Some ornithologists claim their brilliant plumage is matchless among all birds. Monals have one genus, *Lophophorus*, consisting of several species. The most famous is the green-tailed monal, commonly known as the Chinese monal pheasant (*L. lhuysii*). Since it is fond of eating the bulb of fritillary, it is known as "fritillary chicken" in China. It is regarded as a first-grade national protected animal and a V-class endangered animal in the international Red Book.

Yellow-bellied tragopan

Crimson-bellied tragopan

White-eared pheasant (or Tibetan pheasant)

Eared Pheasant

Another genus of rare and precious pheasants in China, *Crossoptilon*, is called horse pheasant in Chinese, but its formal zoological name is eared pheasant. It is probably called horse pheasant because it has a bushy tail like a horse's tail. The name eared pheasant comes from prolonged ear coverts that look like ears.

The genus consists of three species, all found in China: (1) The white eared-pheasant (*C. crossoptilon*), found in Tibet, Qinghai, Sichuan and Yunnan, is also called Tibetan eared-pheasant, because it is chiefly found in Tibet. (2) The blue eared-pheasant (*C. auritum*), found in Qinghai, Gansu and Ningxia, was nominated as Ningxia's provincial bird. (3) The brown eared-pheasant are found only in the region between Shanxi and Hebei provinces. The three species have different

A pair of blue-eared pheasants

Brown-eared pheasant

colors and morphological features, but in terms of value and fame the brown eared-pheasant rises above the others. This is not because of its color (brown is more homely than blue or white, which are also mixed with red and purple) or its size (it is the smallest of the three), but primarily because its range is much more restricted and its population much smaller. Another factor is historical. It was a "famous bird" as early as the Han Dynasty (206 B.C.-A.D.220). Rulers used the tail feathers of the brown eared-pheasant to decorate the helmets of their faithful and gallant officers, especially as awards, for generals' military achievements. The significance of a brown eared-pheasant helmet was to both commend meritorious warriors and encourage them to have a fighting spirit "as gallant as the brown eared-pheasant's." It was said that the brown eared-pheasant, once engaged in fighting, would rather die than

Brown-eared pheasants

Silver pheasant

give up the fight.

Such awards continued for thousands of years until the Qing Dynasty (1644-1911). In the meantime, tail feathers of the brown eared-pheasant were exported to foreign countries at good selling prices. A pair of brown eared-pheasants was said to be worth one thousand silver dollars in European markets at that time.

Silver and Swinhoe's Pheasants

Finally, there are several species of pheasants that belong to the genus *Lophura*.

Two particularly well-known species are the silver pheasant and Swinhoe's pheasant.

The silver pheasant (*L. nycthemera*) has been widely exhibited in zoological gardens abroad because its plumage is chiefly white, unlike that of other pheasants with different colors that dazzle the eyes. The silver pheasant displays only three basic colors: white (neck, back and tail), blue (throat, chest and belly), and red (head, legs and feet). Though the colors and patterns are simple, they are very harmonious and pleasing to the eye. Swinhoe's pheasant (*L. swinhoei*) is similar in basic morphology, but different in coloring. Although the colors are also limited to red, white and blue, they are markedly brilliant and predominantly blue, therefore more attractive.

Another difference is that, whereas the silver pheasant is widely distributed and has a large population, Swinhoe's pheasant is limited to the island of Taiwan and has a very small population. It is as endangered as the mikado pheasant of Taiwan and is regarded as a first-grade national protected animal.

Crested ibis calling at dusk

The Crested Ibis

The crested ibis is not only the rarest and most precious bird in China, but also the rarest and most precious bird in the world. It is not endemic to China. Its scientific name, *Nipponia nippon*, clearly reflects that, but neither is it endemic to Japan, despite its name. Its original distribution was broad, from northern to southern East Asia, or to be more specific, from the Russian Far East through northeast China, the D.P.R. of Korea and the Japanese islands to Taiwan and Hainan. It also had sizable populations. Then, how did it become the rarest and most precious bird in the world? Unrestricted hunting and destruction of the natural environment gradually caused this widely distributed bird to disappear from its various habitats. By the spring of 1981 it was generally accepted that no crested ibises existed in China, Russia and Korea and only five remained on a lone island in Niigata Prefecture in northern Japan. Various interested circles began to make plans and take action to rescue the bird. For instance, the world's ornithological society designated it as a "major animal" under international protection; the Japanese Board of Environmental Protection adopted a "tactical action" by which all five remaining crested ibises were captured and concentrated in a newly established crested ibis conservation center, with the intention to preserve its existence. In the meantime the Chinese Academy of Sciences had joined the effort to rescue the bird by dispatching a search group to investigate whether any crested ibises remained in China, although the bird had not been seen for 20 years. In three years the group traveled more than 50,000 kilometers in nine provinces in east, central, north, northwest and northeast China. The search was fruitless until May 1981, when the group finally discovered two nests of crested ibises in Jinjiahe Valley and Yaojia Gully in Yangxian County.

Altogether seven birds were found, including both adults and young, indicating that the species not only was not extinct, but had breeding capability, so that its continued existence was viable.

With a body 77 centimeters long, the crested ibis is a medium-sized bird. It is also a very beautiful bird. When young, it is pale gray, gradually turning white with soft, pinkish sheen when adult. Its face and crown are scarlet, the underparts of the wings and tail are also a brilliant scarlet, and the legs and feet are a deeper red. Since its body is mostly red, becoming more obvious when it flies, it is also called "scarlet heron" in its native habitat and has won the epithet of "beautiful gem of the Orient" in foreign countries.

Besides designating the crested ibis as a first-grade national protected animal, the Chinese government set up an observation station for conservation of the crested ibis in Yangxian County, Shaanxi Province.

Under its good care new nests and new broods of crested ibises increased every year to more than 40 in 1990. The Chinese also signed agreements of international cooperation with related institutions in Japan and Germany, which promised financial aid for setting up crested ibis captive breeding center in Yangxian County where Japanese and German bird specialists will visit every year for observation and research.

It seems very likely the hard life of this bird is already over, and its future days will be better and better.

Crested ibis feeding young birds

Amphibians and Reptiles

Yangtze alligators

China's amphibian species account for only 6.6 percent of the world's total, and the reptilian species are even fewer, 5.5 percent. The reason for their low percentages is chiefly geographic restriction. The distribution of amphibians and, especially, reptiles is fundamentally in tropical and subtropical regions, gradually extending to a wider area.

Since only a small portion of China's territory is located in the tropical and subtropical sphere, the amphibian species naturally are few.

Endemic species are also few, with only the Yangtze alligator, the alligator lizard, and the giant salamander worth mentioning.

Yangtze Alligator

More than 20 species of crocodiles and alligators exist in the world, all relic animals. The reason the Yangtze alligator, endemic to China, has become

the most famous among them is simply that China has the most ancient culture. As early as several thousand years ago records appeared in ancient Chinese books about this animal, but its original name was not *yangzi'e*, which is a transliteration of its foreign name, but *tuo*, a name that can be traced back not only to such ancient books as *Book of*

Songs and *Book of Rites*, but even to inscriptions on bones or tortoiseshells in the Shang and Yin (16th-11th century B.C.) dynasties. The ancient Chinese believed it was a variety of dragon. For instance, Li Shizhen called it *tuolong* (*tuo* dragon) in his *Compendium of Materia Medica*, but the common people called it *zhupolong* (pig woman dragon) or *tulong* (earth dragon).

Since it was believed to be a dragon, it was given super powers by the people, such as being able to fly horizontally, but not vertically, and to spray fog and rain.

Furthermore, from ancient records we know that as early as the Zhou Dynasty (11th century-221 B.C.) people used its hide to make drums and its meat was said to be palatable. According to textual research, the custom of eating alligator meat continued until the end of the Ming Dynasty (1368-1644).

However, the name *tuo* is rarely used today by Chinese periodicals, except for a few scholarly publications. The character for *tuo* is just too difficult to write, recognize or even pronounce, hence it is far less acceptable than *yangzi'e*, despite it's being translated from a foreign name.

First among the factors that account for the preciousness of this animal is its antiquity. Crocodiles and alligators began their golden age as early as the Cretaceous period, when the world's animals were still under the reign of the dinosaurs.

Later on, after the dinosaurs were completely wiped out by an unknown catastrophe, the crocodilians remained intact and were able to continue their existence, despite innumerable crises and hardships, until now. Can anyone deny their invaluable worth as real "living fossils"?

Another important factor in judging the value of an animal is its rarity. This factor is also quite outstanding in the Yangtze alligator, since it is the rarest and most endangered of all existing crocodilians. It has long been designated by international

Yangtze alligators at rest

Newly hatched Yangtze alligators

conservation organizations as an E-class endangered animal and a species on the first-class trade-prohibition list.

Its population was never known clearly before 1949, but surveys since the 1950s revealed that the majority of remnant Yangtze alligators were concentrated in swamps and branches of the Yangtze River in southern Anhui Province, with very few left in Jiangsu and Zhejiang provinces. An investigation in Anhui Province in 1976 found only a few dozen, leading to rumors abroad that the Yangtze alligator was already extinct. Such rumors soon proved to be unfounded. Anhui Zoologists made a four-month survey in 1981 and found approximately 200 alligators. There is even more promising news concerning the conservation work with captive alligators.

The first Yangtze alligator breeding farm in China was founded in 1979 at Xuancheng in Anhui Province. It was enlarged and reorganized as the Yangtze Alligator Breeding Research Center in 1982, with a national nature reserve attached to it. By early 1990 it covered an area of about a hundred hectares, with nearly 30,000 alligators in captivity.

Yangtze alligators usually mate and lay eggs in late spring and early summer, laying 30 to 40 eggs in each batch. Since natural hatching often suffers from bad weather and natural enemies, the research center has successfully used artificial hatching, which requires only one month for each brood.

The first generation of alligators began to lay eggs in 1988, and the first artificial hatching took place in 1989. The 22 young alligators were all released to the wild in May 1989. After six months' continued observation these second-generation alligators were confirmed to be growing satisfactorily in the wild under the protection of the conservation technicians, so they are expected to grow up as wild alligators in the future.

Alligator-lizard in Yaoshan County,Guangxi Zhuang Autonomous Region

Alligator-lizard

As indicated by its name, it is a small reptilian animal that looks like both an alligator and a lizard. Its head looks like a lizard's, but its body looks like an alligator's. Moreover, its laterally flattened tail looks particularly like an alligator's tail.

However, whereas a Yangtze alligator is about two meters long and weighs nearly 50 kilograms, an alligator-lizard is only 30 to 40 centimeters long and weighs less than one kilogram. The alligator-lizard is, nevertheless, also a second-grade national

protected animal and renowned animal in the world, for it has peculiarities in both geographic distribution and taxonomic position. According to taxonomists, it belongs to a mono-subfamily, monogenus and monospecies of the family Lacertidae. This family has four species of lizards. Except for the alligator-lizard, found only in a corner of Guangxi Zhuang Autonomous Region, China, other species are all found in countries across the Pacific, namely, Mexico and Guatemala. Such peculiar animal distribution is rarely found in zoogeography.

The alligator-lizard is also known as the Yaoshan (Yao Mountain) alligator-lizard, because the first specimen was discovered in the Dayao Mountains in eastern Guangxi in 1928. For many years it was believed that Jinxiu Autonomous County was the only place where the alligator-lizard lived, but more were later found in Zhaoping and Hexian counties, east of Jinxiu Autonomous County. However, the population of alligator-lizards has always been small. An estimate made by a general survey team in 1983 suggested the total numbers in the wild could not be more than a few hundred.

Up to the early 1990s, only Chinese zoological gardens had alligator-lizards on exhibition; no foreign zoological gardens or aquariums—more than a thousand in the world—had ever kept one for exhibition. Experience gained by the Beijing Zoo has shown that, by proper keeping and management,

Giant salamander

be one to two meters long and weigh 30 to 40 kilograms. Some aquariums have super giant salamanders 50 to 60 years old and over 50 kilogram in weight —a real wonder.

alligator-lizards can not only live and survive in a zoo, but also breed. They mate in early spring. As ovoviviparous animals, they give birth at the end of December or early in January, each litter consisting of four to seven lizards.

Giant Salamander

This is a very contradictory animal. Although it is the most important and most outstanding member of the class Amphibia, the largest and most grotesquely shaped of the more than 3,000 species of amphibians, it used to be freely sold and bought in Chinese markets and freely served in Chinese restaurants.

These were common practices in China until a few years ago, when the Chinese government made it a second-grade national protected animal.

Even specialists who compiled the international Red Book, or IUCN Red List of Threatened Animals, had difficulty giving it its correct position in the list. They finally determined to designate it as an I-class animal. "I" represents "indeterminate," which means "there is not enough information to say which of the three official categories (E=endangered, V=vulnerable, R=rare) is appropriate."

An adult giant salamander may

图书在版编目(CIP)数据

中国珍稀动物:英文/谭邦杰著.
－北京:新世界出版社,1996.1
ISBN 7-80005-298-2

Ⅰ.中…
Ⅱ.谭…
Ⅲ.珍稀动物-中国-画册-英文
Ⅳ.Q95

中国珍稀动物

谭邦杰　著

＊

新世界出版社出版
(北京百万庄路 24 号)
外文印刷厂彩印分厂印刷
中国国际图书贸易总公司发行
(中国北京车公庄西路 35 号)
北京邮政信箱第 399 号　邮政编码 100044
1996 年(英文)第一版
ISBN 7-80005-298-2
08000
85-E-467P